Then . . .

RIGHT, WE'RE OFF NOW. OH, AND BY THE WAY, MIKE HAS ANOTHER BROTHER, BEN. HE'S PLAYING FOOTBALL AT THE MOMENT. WE SAID HE SHOULD MEET YOU IN THE CAFE IN ABOUT AN HOUR.

WHAT? HOW WILL I KNOW WHO HE IS?

THE KIDS WILL RECOGNISE HIM. DON'T WORRY. 'BYE!

SOME MATE SHE TURNED OUT TO BE! I KNOW SHE AND MIKE WANTED SOME TIME BY THEMSELVES, BUT I DIDN'T REALISE SHE WAS PLANNING ON CLEARING OFF QUITE SO SOON. AND I BET THIS BEN WILL BE ABOUT 13 AND THINK BURPING'S THE HEIGHT OF ENTERTAINMENT. GREAT!

OK, THEN, WE'D BETTER GET STARTED. WHAT WOULD YOU LIKE TO SEE FIRST?

THE ELEPHANTS.

NO, THE LIONS.

I SEE. WELL, SINCE YOU CAN'T AGREE ON ANYTHING WE'LL VISIT THE CHILDREN'S ZOO FIRST. THERE'LL BE LOTS OF INTERESTING ANIMALS TO SEE THERE.

I HOPE!

But they weren't impressed . . .

THAT WAS BORING. I WANT TO SEE THE ELEPHANTS.

NAH. THE LIONS ARE THE BEST. LET'S GO AND SEE THEM.

OK, LET ME HAVE A LOOK AT THE MAP AND SEE WHERE THEY ARE.

THE ELEPHANTS AND LIONS ARE AT OPPOSITE ENDS OF THE ZOO. IT'LL MEAN A LONG WALK.

BUT I DON'T WANT TO SEE THE LIONS!

AND I DON'T WANT TO SEE THE ELEPHANTS!

HECK. I'VE ONLY BEEN HERE HALF AN HOUR AND THEY'RE DRIVING ME CRAZY ALREADY. WHAT ON EARTH AM I GOING TO DO WHEN THE OTHER HORROR FINISHES PLAYING FOOTBALL? ELAINE COULD AT LEAST HAVE GIVEN ME A HAND FOR A LITTLE WHILE.

continued on page 94

cont

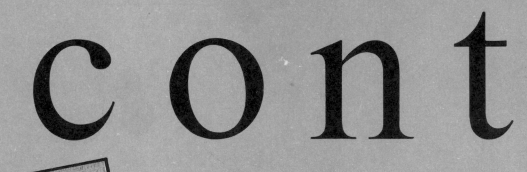

THE ART OF PARTIES! p18

ents

2nd TIME
AROUND
p90

LET'S HEAR IT FOR THE BOYS!

For all that we love them, you must admit that boys are a bit . . . well . . . strange sometimes. They have their own ways of doing and saying things that make no sense whatsoever to us girls. Until now, that is — and the Patches guide to finally figuring boys out!

BOYS can eat as many chips, cakes, crisps and sweets as they like and never put on an ounce. This is one of the most annoying facts known to womankind. There is little you can do about it, however, so try not to console yourself by keeping up with him on a binge.

Boys say, "I'll call you" the way you and I say "I love George Michael". Both sayings don't really mean anything, there's less than a 99% chance of them ever coming to anything and you usually only say them to agree with someone. Some boys, however, have been been known to promise to phone simply to get away from the girl they're speaking to!

"I've got football that night." This is an excuse that boys use a lot. In fact, bring up the subject of meeting your gran, going to your house for tea or your cousin's wedding and you can be sure he'll have a game on that night that is life or death to his team's chances in the league. It doesn't matter what night you pick, he'll already be booked up. The only way to get round this one is to join his football team as soon as you can.

Boys like to maintain the illusion that they look good all the time and hardly spend five minutes in the bathroom before dashing out on a date. They do this so that you'll look bad because you were still brushing on your mascara when he came to the door. There is only one thing you can do to put an end to this and that is enlist the help of his sister and a stopwatch. Get her to time him applying his hair gel, fixing his badges just so on his denim jacket and posing in front of the mirror. Then just laugh loudly next time he taps his foot impatiently — he won't have a leg to stand on!

Boys are always better at maths than girls. This is not an insult to girls, it's just that boys have such a head start in the subject they find it slightly easier. Let's face it, anyone who can understand team A playing team B and the winner playing C or D, depending on goal aggregate, *must* have a better chance of understanding maths!

Boys always maintain that music isn't music unless it's heavy metal and the

volume is at maximum. The reason for this is obvious — if you're sitting in his room listening to records you've got a fat chance of talking, haven't you? Every time you steer the conversation round to touchy subjects like "Do you really love me?" he can pretend not to hear and give you a kiss instead. Our advice is to wear ear plugs and enjoy the smooching!

Slow records at discos are a totally different story. Boys in general wouldn't be caught dead kissing a girl during a smoochy record on the dancefloor. What d'you mean that sounds nice! Don't be silly — kiss you in public? He'd sooner have someone steal the rusty hubcabs off his beloved old banger!

Boys have the unfortunate habit of wanting what they don't have. This is why he nearly drowns in a glass of Coke when a tall blonde waltzes past him at the disco and you're standing at his elbow fuming. Console yourself with the comforting thought that the blonde girl didn't even look his way, and then spend the rest of the night looking round to see if you see anyone ... serves him right!

A boy and his friends are like Madonna and bleach. You can't separate one from the other without a lot of fuss and arguments. The sooner you realise this, the better it will be for all concerned. There is no point in breaking your heart when he won't come shopping on Saturday afternoon with you because he's watching his mate play rugby in the pouring rain. He won't understand why you're getting so upset about it and will tell his friend that you're starting to get clingy — the kiss of death!

The very thought of a romantic soppy film is enough to make the average boy break out in a cold sweat. Sit through two hours of people kissing and rubbish like that? Yeuch! The only way you'll get him to accompany you to the cinema is to lie and convince him, once you're both seated comfortably, that you honestly thought it was "Zombies Chainsaw Massacre on Hallowe'en, Part 2" and you're really sorry but you've paid the money now and you may as well stay.

Boys tend to be very touchy about their clothes. When they think they've hit on a trendy winning outfit, well that's it. No matter how hard you try, you will not convince him that a football top does not look right under a dress jacket. The only way round this is to resort to subtle persuasion — buy him a shirt you like and tell him you're going out with Hunky Harry unless he wears it.

One last thing — boys can be very devious creatures, so make sure none of them get their hands on this feature ... After all, how else are you going to stay one jump ahead?

Four's A Crowd

So . . .

OH, ALL RIGHT THEN. YOU'VE CONVINCED ME. IT'LL BE A LAUGH IF NOTHING ELSE.

THANKS A MILLION. SEE YOU AT THE RINK AT TWO O'CLOCK.

On Saturday . . .

WE'RE OFF FOR A SKATE, THEN. SEE YOU.

BUT, CRAIG . . .

WELL, WHAT DO I DO FIRST?

WHAT D'YOU MEAN, WHAT DO YOU DO? HOW SHOULD I KNOW? I THOUGHT YOU COULD SKATE.

BUT TINA SAID YOU'D TEACH ME . . .

THAT'LL BE RIGHT! I'VE NEVER SKATED BEFORE IN MY LIFE!

WELL, WE MAY AS WELL TRY. THERE'S NO POINT IN STANDING HERE FOR THE REST OF THE AFTERNOON.

HI, YOU TWO! HOW'RE YOU DOING?

ROTTEN! I WANT A WORD WITH YOU, CRAIG.

SHE CAN'T SKATE EITHER. WHAT AM I SUPPOSED TO DO?

JUST PUSH OFF ON THE ICE AND LEAN FORWARD A BIT. IT'S EASY.

I THOUGHT YOU SAID PAUL WOULD TEACH ME. TURNS OUT HE'S AS HOPELESS AS ME.

WELL, YOU'LL HAVE FUN LEARNING TOGETHER.

WELL, COME ON, THEN. I SUPPOSE WE'D BETTER GIVE IT A TRY.

Continued on page 12

9

LOOK TO THE

Ever spent hours and hours poring over hair magazines or old copies of Patches looking for the perfect hairstyle?

Well, search no further — we've got all the answers! Just find your star sign below and you'll have the style you've always wanted!

ARIES
(March 21 — April 20)

Arians have very active lifestyles and are always rushing around from one place to another, barely stopping to take a breath.

You love to be the centre of attraction so you like to know you look good, but with the minimum of fuss.

Your style of dress is modern but not outrageous and you're usually to be found in jeans or other practical clothes — no frilly blouses for you!

The ideal hairstyle for you is something short, adaptable and easy to keep, like this one which was styled using Schwarzkopf's Accent gel.

Wash it every day, towel dry, rub in a blob of gel and all you need is a quick blast with the hairdrier to keep it looking great all day long.

TAURUS
(April 21 — May 21)

Taureans are hard-working, reliable and they love money!

Whatever they do, they try hard to make it an outstanding success and like nothing more than being in charge.

If you're a Taurean you probably spend quite a lot of money on your appearance, as it's important to you.

Make-up is something you're not particularly interested in but you do use it.

As for hairstyles, you probably visit the hairdresser regularly and use an expensive salon where you know you will be pampered.

This cut is ideal for you. It's modern but classy and doesn't need too much attention. To jazz it up a little, it's been coloured using Schwarzkopf's Igo Fleur Red Mahogany, which isn't too loud for your fairly conservative taste.

GEMINI
(May 22 — June 21)

People born under Gemini are the type you find dancing on tables at parties one week and sitting in the corner sulking the next.

Because of your changeable moods, you probably have a wardrobe full of clothes you bought and wore once (or didn't wear at all) and a drawer rattling with unused make-up.

You like to look trendy and a bit mysterious (let's face it, you're a bit of a poser!), and the thing you like about make-up is how different it can make you look.

This style is great for Geminis — the rich colour prevents it looking too boring and as it's not too heavily layered, you can tie it up, curl it, straighten it, leave it loose — the possibilities are endless.

CANCER
(June 22 — July 22)

Well, let's face facts here — you're just a little bit vain! Your looks are very important to you and you spend a lot of time thinking about your image.

You wouldn't dream of stepping outside the door in an outfit you threw together and when you buy a skirt you want a blouse to match, a pair of shoes and well, a new bag wouldn't go amiss, would it?

Make-up is almost a hobby to you. You wear it most days and love experimenting with new colours.

You'll love this style by Pierre Alexandre because it's glamorous and feminine and gives you the opportunity to play around with lots of mousse, gel and hairspray.

Dried with a blob of mousse, it'll look great for school or work.

LEO
(July 24 — August 23)

Leo people are the most confident of the zodiac. They like to think they're better than everyone else but that doesn't make them arrogant — just happy that they're obviously superior!

If you're a Leo you're a bit of a clothes snob and would much rather spend your money in an expensive shop than in one of the cheaper chain stores. You love it when people admire your clothes and you can say, "What, these old shoes? They only cost £40."

The same goes for make-up. You'd much rather buy one RoC lipstick than three Rimmel ones and you choose classy, elegant colours — no fuchsia pink for you!

Strangely enough, like lions, most Leos have curly hair and you'll love the style above as it's fairly versatile.

If your hair isn't naturally curly, perhaps you should consider a perm, which will help keep your hair looking good all the time.

VIRGO
(August 24 — September 23)

If you're a Virgo, you'll be a very organised, practical person who hates mess.

You like your wardrobe to be as well-organised as your life and probably have lots of skirts, tops and blouses which mix and match with each other. You never impulse buy, but think about everything carefully before you spend your hard-earned cash.

Make-up isn't something you spend a lot of money on, because you don't wear make-up every day and tend to use the same colours every time you do.

When it comes to haircuts, you visit the hairdresser regularly because you hate to look untidy.

A practical bob like the one above is great for Virgos, because it doesn't need too much looking after and is always neat and unfussy.

You're not too keen on dyed hair (you think it looks a bit tacky), but if you do decide to change your hair colour, you'll visit a salon for some subtle highlights or a vegetable rinse.

STARS...

LIBRA
(September 24 — October 24)

Like Cancer, Librans are a bit over-obsessed with their appearance but not for vanity's sake. While Cancers worry about what others think of the way they look, Librans just can't enjoy themselves if they don't look their best.

When it comes to clothes shopping, Librans are the girls you see charging all over the town flitting from one shop to another in a panic — they can't make up their mind what to buy! If you're a Libran you probably have lots of clothes which don't match anything else you wear, just because you bought them in a last-minute panic!

You love experimenting with make-up and never wear just a bit of mascara and smudge of lipstick. If you wear make-up, you wear the works!

You like your hair to look natural and glossy and prefer mid-length cuts which are feminine.

If you colour your hair, you probably use henna or vegetable rinses and as you detest falseness, you'd never dream of having a very drastic colour change or a really outrageous style.

SCORPIO
(October 24 — November 22)

Scorpio people are very attractive to the opposite sex and the way they look reflects this.

Scorpios take a lot of care over their appearance and like to look glamorous and mysterious.

If you're a Scorpio, you like dark colours for clothes and well-cut, tailored styles which show off your figure. Even just for school or work, you try to look as good as possible.

You'll very rarely see a Scorpio without make-up on and when they go out, they really go to town. You probably have lots of make-up and have a different set look for different occasions.

Scorpio girls often have long hair which is in good condition and very shiny.

You'll like this style, created using Alberto VO5 styling products, as it's quite classy and elegant. It doesn't worry you if your hair takes a long time to style — you reckon all the hard work is worth it if you look great when it's finished.

SAGITTARIUS
(November 23 — December 21)

Sagittarians are friendly and outgoing — the life and soul of the party.

If you're a Sagittarian, you probably look a bit 'arty' and dress in muted colours or black. You prefer casual clothes and would choose 501's over a cocktail dress any time.

You love make-up — it's practically an art form to you and you can quite happily spend hours in front of the mirror experimenting with different looks.

Your hair could be in almost any style but there's one thing for sure — it won't look natural! You have your hair cut often — and rarely in the same style twice!

You'll like this style from Taylor Ferguson of Glasgow because it's smart, up-to-date and dare we say it, trendy!

CAPRICORN
(December 22 — January 20)

Capricorns are usually good at sport and are often members of sports clubs — just as much for the social life as for the actual sport.

Because of this you have two very different sets of clothes — one side of the wardrobe full of sweatshirts, jogging trousers and training shoes, the other packed with slinky, sexy clothes and high-heeled shoes.

Your daytime make-up is natural and healthy-looking but for special nights out, you love to go to town with sparkly eyeshadows and glossy lipstick.

Because of your lifestyle, you need an adaptable haircut like the one shown here.

It will look great just washed and blow-dried with a blob of mousse during the day but, for evening, some gel rubbed through with your fingers will mould it into this glamorous style.

AQUARIUS
(January 21 — February 19)

Aquarius is the most extrovert sign of the zodiac and the way you dress reflects this.

You don't mind how weird you look to others so long as you're happy and, although you dress pretty outrageously, you couldn't care less when people point or stare.

You enjoy wearing make-up to match your clothes and probably have a favourite make-up for each outfit you own.

You care a lot about the way your hair looks and spend lots of time flicking through hair magazines and looking at hair dye colour charts. You're a bit mistrustful of hairdressers though and sometimes chicken out of a drastic change in case something goes wrong and your image is ruined!

This style by Charlie Miller is just the kind of cut you like — different and with a lot of colour to jazz it up.

PISCES
(February 21 — March 20)

Pisces people are the romantic dreamers of the zodiac and Piscean girls are usually feminine and romantic-looking.

Your wardrobe is full of soft jumpers and floaty skirts in pastel shades of blue, pink and mint green and in summer, you practically live in white!

Obviously, with this style of dress, your make-up can't be too way out and you love soft shades of blue, pink or peach. You never look too made-up and people often wonder if you're wearing any make-up at all.

Pisceans love long hair so they can tie it up in lacy scarves or pretty ribbons and their hair is always clean and sweet-smelling.

This style from Pierre Alexandre is perfect for Pisceans as it's soft, natural and very romantic looking — just the thing for long walks in the countryside!

But . . .

OOOH!

WATCH WHAT YOU'RE DOING!

THAT WASN'T VERY CLEVER, WAS IT? WHAT DID YOU PULL MY ARM FOR?

I LIKE THAT! I WAS ALL RIGHT TILL YOU GRABBED AT ME.

COME ON! JUST BE MORE CAREFUL THIS TIME.

HE MAY BE GOOD-LOOKING, BUT HE HASN'T GOT MUCH OF A SENSE OF HUMOUR, THAT'S FOR SURE.

Then . . .

HEY, WATCH OUT!

THESE BEGINNERS ARE A PAIN. THEY KEEP GETTING IN YOUR WAY.

THAT'S IT, I'VE HAD ENOUGH.

C'MON, PAUL. GIVE IT ANOTHER TRY.

WHAT? WITH YOU? YOU'RE USELESS.

ME! YOU'RE USELESS, YOU MEAN. WHY DID YOU COME IF YOU DIDN'T EVEN WANT TO TRY?

CRAIG ASKED ME AND I COULDN'T GET OUT OF IT. I'D RATHER BE SOMEWHERE WATCHING FOOTBALL. SEE YOU!

RUDE CREEP! I'D BETTER TRY TO FIND TINA. I MIGHT AS WELL GO HOME.

But suddenly . . .

WHY DON'T YOU LOOK WHERE YOU'RE GOING? YOU SHOULD STAY OFF THE ICE IF YOU CAN'T SKATE!

SORRY.

Leaving Me Now

For a long time, I'd known Paul was unhappy. But I didn't think he was as unhappy as this . . .

The town was at its best at night. Especially at this time of year. The pavements were wet, and they shone black under the street lights. The shop windows were bright with tinsel and Santas, and ornate Christmas decorations were strung across the High Street. The flashing lights danced blue and red and green on the black puddles. I shoved my hands deeper into my pockets and hunched my shoulders against the spitting rain and cold wind. I liked the wintertime.

I turned the corner by Virgin to go down to the bus station. I'd had a phone call from Paul, my boyfriend, asking me to meet him there at half past seven. It was a bit strange — I only saw Paul a couple of times a week, and at weekends. He liked time on his own, and so did I. I reckoned it must be something pretty serious if he wanted to see me on a night off.

I never dreamed how serious.

The bus station coffee bar was warm, full of people and smoke. It stung my eyes for the first few seconds after the clean night air, but soon the smoke seemed to clear a bit, and I spotted Paul sitting at a table by the jukebox. I pushed my way through and sat down opposite him.

A Reader's True Story

Continued on page 16

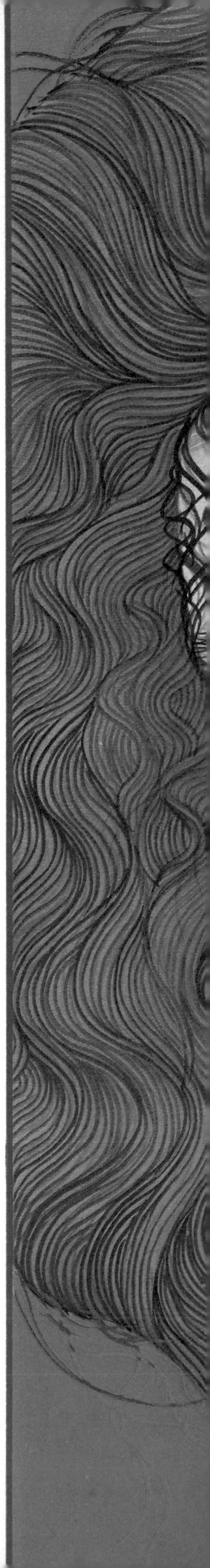

Leaving Me Now

Continued from page 14

"Hi, Paul," I said. He glanced up briefly then carried on gazing at his coffee. I just waited. I knew the routine by now.

Paul and I had been going out for seven months. We met at school, but we weren't in any of each others' classes. In all that time, I'd never known him get through a month without a crisis. He'd been thrown out of his house at least nine times since he was fifteen.

Things were always sorted out pretty quickly, but never permanently. Paul was a lovely guy — he just couldn't get on with his parents.

Finally he looked up. I smiled. "Come on then. What's wrong?"

Those dark blue eyes, troubled, all grave. I'd almost stopped taking him seriously.

"It's Dad again, Gail. I can't stand him. I can't live in the same house as him any longer."

"What did you fight about this time?"

"Her, again. I can't stand her. Always poking her nose in where it's not wanted, tidying my stuff, nagging. It's my house, not hers."

I forgot to mention that. Paul's mum died when he was about seven, and his dad remarried. Paul hated his stepmother, although she always seemed OK to me.

"So what happened?"

"I called her an interfering old slag, and Dad took a swipe at me."

I was shocked. "He never hit you?"

Paul turned his head and showed me a bruise developing on his cheekbone. "Over that whingeing —" He stopped, scowling. I knew he felt as if his dad and his stepmother were ganging up against him. And I must admit I was surprised that his dad had hit him. He'd never done that before.

"So what now?" I said.

"That's it. That is absolutely the last straw. I'm leaving."

"Oh yeah." I was sceptical. "And where are you going to go?"

"London."

"What?" I'd expected him to ask if he could stay with us for a while, or to say he would stay with his sister. I was quiet for a while, wondering when he was planning to go. We had all sorts of things arranged for Christmas. I had his present already, wrapped up and waiting at home. My mum had even invited him round for Christmas dinner, knowing that things were bound to be strained for him at home.

"Mum, you're brilliant!" I'd told her, knowing how much store she set on a "family Christmas".

"Yes, well. Just because Paul doesn't have a happy home life doesn't mean it's like that for everyone."

I'd been really looking forward to Christmas. But now something told me it was going to be a sad day this year.

Paul looked up from his cup of coffee. "I'm leaving tonight, on the nine o'clock coach. I want you to come with me."

For a moment, I couldn't speak. All the other travellers in the café were chatting and shouting and laughing, unaware of the importance of our conversation. In a panic, I thought about earlier this evening when I'd been sitting at home with Mum watching TV when the telephone had disturbed the peace . . .

"Gail, is that you?"

"Paul? Where are you?" He was calling from a phonebox.

"I'm in town. Can you meet me at the bus station?"

I could picture him standing in the booth, his spiky fair hair wet from the rain, his leather jacket zipped right up against the cold. I smiled down the receiver, thinking how much I liked him.

"Yeah, OK. What time?"

"Half past seven. I'll see you in the café."

"Who was that, Gail?" Mum called from the living room as I hung up.

"Oh, it was Paul. I'm meeting him in town. I think he's in trouble again."

"That boy!" Mum said, but not unkindly. "He's never out of trouble. You'll never change that."

I was worried, though. What was wrong this time?

And now I knew. Paul was running away to London, and he wanted me to go along with him.

"At least you haven't said no," Paul said suddenly, grinning. I laughed and relaxed a bit. "Think about it. I'll get you a coffee."

I watched him push through the crowds of rucksacks to the counter, waving a pound note at the harassed waitress. I thought of how life would be without him — and suddenly, shockingly, I realised I didn't want a life without him.

I thought about Mum waiting at home, watching TV. At nine o'clock she'd make some supper and take the dog out. The way it had always been. The way it would always be. Predictable. Safe. Dull.

What if I never went home? What if I just went missing? Other teenagers just went missing and were never found. What about me, though? Would I keep in touch or just vanish forever?

And what about money? Where would we live?

They say you should grab opportunities. Life is for living, you should get out and see the world. Live life for yourself.

And then there was Paul. He was here, with me now, and I didn't want to let him go . . . all these thoughts whirled round in my head as I made my decision, knowing that life could never be the same . . .

* * *

The bus growled out of the station, pushing its way into the line of traffic. A shudder ran through me. What would it be like never to see these streets again? My reflection stared back at me from the black, grimy window, sad and troubled. This was my town, my home.

We passed the cinema, where Paul and I had gone on our first date. The traffic lights which never seemed to stay on green for more than three seconds. The shop where I'd bought my first court shoes.

This town had been my home all my life, and I wasn't ready to leave it yet. Not even for Paul.

I pictured the other bus, the express, on the motorway to London. Taking Paul out of my life.

The decorations flashed overhead as the bus pulled in at my stop.

"Happy Christmas, luv," the conductor said, as I passed him.

"Yeah," I said, choking, "Happy Christmas."

FRUITY BEAUTY

Ditch the chocolate habit for good by substituting exotic fruits. The fibre in such things as apples will keep you feeling full longer, and extra vitamins will do wonders for your skin. The beauty bonuses don't end there, though, as fruit can be a useful addition to your beauty routine. Read on . . .

ORANGES AND LEMONS . . .

● Dried orange and lemon peel can be added to your bath to give it a fresh scent.
● Strained lemon juice added to the final rinse when you wash your hair gives it extra shine and sparkle.
● Lemon cleanser can be made from mixing a tablespoon of natural yoghurt with a teaspoon of lemon juice. Remember to rinse it off with water, though.
● You can make up an Orange Scrub with a tablespoon each of finely chopped orange peel, ground almonds and oatmeal. Mix them together with water to make a paste and gently rub into the skin. Rinse off with fresh water.
● Lemon juice also makes a pretty good setting lotion if you're using rollers on your hair.

AN APPLE A DAY . . .

● Hair Tonic made from a tablespoon of pure apple juice with three of water can be massaged into the scalp after washing your hair to cure dandruff.

STRAWBERRY FAYRE . . .

● If you can bear not to eat them, strawberries make a good face-mask for combination skins. Mash a few strawberries with enough ground oatmeal to make a thick paste and leave it on your face for about ten minutes.
● If you're caught without your toothbrush, half a strawberry wiped over your teeth will sweeten your breath — but it's only a temporary measure, don't forget!

If all this seems like too much effort, you can always eat the fruit and head off to your nearest "Body Shop" instead!

B

FANCY dress parties are always a good bet if you're fed-up seeing the same old faces. And you can be reasonably sure that everyone will enter into the spirit of the thing if you suggest a theme when you're doling out invitations. To help you out, we've put together a few fancy dress ideas that won't cost the earth, and suggestions on make-up and accessories that should help your party go with a swing!

The
Art
Of
Parties

VICARS AND TARTS

BASICALLY you want to dress up in the tartiest outfit your mother will let you get away with, or if you're a bit shy, or the weather's a bit rough for midriff exposures, you could go a bit flapperish with lots of red lipstick and long straight dresses and beads. The odd feather boa wouldn't go amiss either, and you should be able to get feathery bits from any haberdashery department.

If you're excruciatingly shy, but your boyfriend's game for a laugh, you could go as a vicar, and he could be a tart. Beg or borrow a suit, and make a dog collar from cardboard.

Eats

Tea-cups and saucers are a must, even if you're not actually serving tea, as are sandwiches with the crusts cut off.

Music

You *could* play Harry Secombe's greatest hits, but that really is going too far. Madonna's "Material Girl" or Sinitta's "Toy Boy" (if you can remember that far back), should get the vicars blushing.

Make-Up

Vicars and tarts make-up is pretty easy to do really. Vicars should look as pale and pasty as possible (due to all those hours poring over the Bible and writing sermons).

Use a really pale foundation. Ours is Miners Extra Light foundation in Ivory Fayre. The Reverend Model also wears Charcoal Shadow on his eyes from the Miners Mates in Chalk/Charcoal with a little more brushed along under his cheekbones and a touch on his lips to give that gaunt look.

Tarts' make-up should be LOUD! There's no room for subtlety here! Choose bright bright shades and pile it on.

We've used the pink from the Miners Mates in Peppermint/Raspberry brushed all over the eyelid with just a little of the lilac from the Pacific Pastels Great Shadow Eye Kit, also by Miners. We used this lightly brushed along under the eyebrow to highlight the eyes.

The darkest shade from the Candid Pink Double Blush was used on our tart's cheeks. Don't blend it too well — it should look obvious.

The final touch is to paint on a perfect pout with Miners Passion Flower lipstick and add a fake beauty spot in Jet Set Creative Kohl Crayon.

PYJAMA PARTY

U NLESS you sleep in the buff, you should have the necessary equipment to hand clothes-wise. You could suggest that everyone brings along their teddy as a partner. If this all seems too goody-goody for your rebellious nature, you could turn up in an old quilted dressing gown, curlers, tartan slippers and your grandad's false teeth in a glass of water. (Better ask him first, though. He may be looking forward to his pork chop tonight.)

Eats

Real nursery stuff this — jelly and ice-cream, blancmange served in fancy paper plates so that it dribbles everywhere, Malory Towers type midnight feasts and, of course, lashings and lashings of ginger beer.

Music

"Teddy Bears Picnic", any "Magic Roundabout" or "Walt Disney" albums, "Pyjamarama" by Roxy Music.

Make-Up

The key word here is cute! The sweeter and more innocent you look, the better.

Martin's looking pretty in Miners Amber Extra Light Foundation applied with a dampened sponge just to even out his skin tone. We used a little brown shadow from Miners On Safari Great Shadow Eye Kit along the socket line to give his eyes some definition and two coats of All Weather Mascara in black to show off those long lashes.

Lesley's foundation is Extra Light by Miners in Soft Stone and we used a light dusting of Translucent Pressed Powder to take away any shine.

Keep your eyeshadow subtle if you're trying this look for yourself — we used a very pale lilac in the corners of Lesley's eyes with a touch of pale lemon towards the outer corners and brushed onto the browbone. Both colours are from Miners Pacific Pastels Great Shadow Eye Kit.

Coloured mascara looks great with this sort of make-up (black is much too harsh). We used Miners All Weather Mascara in Forget Me Not.

A baby pink gives lips that soft kissable look (ours is Oyster Shell by Miners), and blusher should be lightly dusted on the top of the cheekbones, just under your eyes. We chose Miners Peacock Pink Soft Blush which is soft enough to be subtle but not so pale it's unnoticeable.

THIS is a variation on the Toga party, but means you don't have to lie around on a couch, eating until you burst. Any sort of hippy dress, especially if it's white, will manage to look a bit Egyptian once you've added plenty of jewellery and fiddled about getting the make-up right. Sandals or bare feet should finish off the effect. Guys can make do with a well-knotted bit of sheeting and a few bangles. A head-dress can be made from a starched remnant stuffed with cotton wool to give it height, topped off with a big brooch. If there's a really boring nerd who you feel compelled to invite, you can always suggest that he comes as a mummy — that way he won't bore anyone by talking to them.

Eats

Spicy dips and lots of fresh fruit and vegetables should be a good bet. Those Egyptians aren't well-preserved for nothing you know!

Music

The Bangles "Walk Like An Egyptian" of course, and the lesser known "Egyptian Reggae" by Jonathan Richmond.

Make-Up

The Egyptians loved pretty eyes and if they weren't lucky enough to have remarkable peepers they just painted thick black lines round them to make them more noticeable.

Our Cleopatra has gold shadow from Miners On Safari Great Shadow Eye Kit brushed lightly across her eyelids and we used Miners Jet Set Creative Kohl Crayon to draw on her black lines.

You'll need a really steady hand for this, so it's probably a good idea to draw a rough outline lightly on both eyes first, then fill it in gradually.

The Egyptians didn't go in much for blusher so don't use any at all. If you feel your face is too 'flat' without it, just brush a little gold shadow under the outer corners of your eyes to highlight your cheekbones.

Lipstick shouldn't be so obvious it takes attention away from the eyes, so use a pale goldish shade. Ours is Miners Pineapple Soda with a little gold shadow brushed onto the centre of both lips for extra emphasis.

Martin's healthy tan helped give him an authentic Egyptian look so all we had to do was brush some gold shadow from the On Safari Great Shadow Eye Kit across his eyelids, on to his cheekbones and over his lips. Two coats of All Weather Black Mascara add the finishing touch.

ANCIENT EGYPTIANS

ANYTHING long, black and grubby should suffice. Don't be tempted to take your pet cat with you, as she probably won't enjoy it, but you could try your hand at making a broomstick. If you're too vain to stick on warts and green make-up, you could always go for a more glamorous look à la Morticia Addams. Joke shops usually have witches' hats and may also have witchy wigs for hire. The zombie look is created by lots of fake blood and Fullers Earth sprinkled liberally over your clothes. This brushes out afterwards as long as you don't get it wet.

Eats

Anything lurid should go down well. You can add red and green food colouring to most things if you want them to look really horrid. Tomato ketchup and juice can be served as gory accompaniments.

Music

"Ghost Busters", "Monster Mash" by Boris Pickett and the Crypt Kickers,"Scary Monsters" by David Bowie and anything by Siouxsie and the Banshees.

MONSTERS MEET

Make-Up

This one's the best fun of the lot! It's definitely not for the vain, because the aim is to make yourself look as horrible as possible!

Martin's zombie look was created using a mixture of Miners cosmetics and specialist stage make-up available from specialist shops and some joke shops.

His face was given a light coating of Vaseline before we applied some liquid latex solution (the Vaseline stops it sticking to the skin!). The latex was painted on then dried with a hairdryer to get the lumpy effect.

Once it was dry, we used a mustard and red/brown shade of eyeshadow from the On Safari Great Shadow Eye Kit over the top to colour the white latex. A light dusting of Miners Translucent Pressed Powder set the shadows, then we used a pair of nail scissors (be careful here!) to cut holes in the latex and leave lots of horrible trailing gungy bits! A liberal sprinkling of Kryolan fake blood and Martin's face could turn your stomach!

Our witch's face was painted totally green using Aqua Color stage make-up but if that's a bit too much for you, just use a really pale foundation like Miners Extra Light in Ivory Fayre.

The horrible shadows on her nose and around her mouth were drawn on using the Charcoal Shadow from Miners Mates Chalk/Charcoal duo with two coats of All Weather Black Mascara for extra emphasis.

Lips look good in a clashing colour — we used Miners Gold Fish which is a pale orange shade.

All make-up by Andrew McLellan using Miners Cosmetics. Wigs by A and A, 9/10 Tanfield, Inverleith Row, Edinburgh. (Tel. 031 556 7057)

THE
MEANING
OF LIFE . . .

According to the Patches Gang!

They're a weird and wonderful lot in the Patches office. Well, you'd have to be to work on a great magazine like this, wouldn't you? At least that's what they keep telling me! I'm the new office junior and I've nicked three whole pages out of the annual to let you into the secret of what they're all like. So here we go, the no-holds barred exposé of the Patches gang . . . And I'm sitting next to the door in case one of them finds out what I'm actually up to!

THE ED

The Ed is a truly wonderful, glamorous being . . . Well, that's what she told me to write anyway! Now that she's nipped out to get her season ticket for the football, however, I can tell you what she's really like. The Ed has been a source of inspiration to me in many ways. Her great time-saving beauty tips are especially good. She simply doesn't bother, and why should she when she can have hours of endless fun picking bits of day old mascara off her eyelashes whenever she fancies it?

Cleanser, toner and moisturiser? Bah! The Ed ignores them all, and still maintains that ageless look. Well, she'd like it to be ageless, but there are a few opinions in the office that date her anywhere from Noah onwards. She keeps the actual date a very closely-guarded secret and rumour has it that her birth certificate is attached to her football season ticket so that no-one else gets their hands on it.

As you may have gathered, the Ed is a great football fan. Not that she likes football in general, you understand, it's just that she loves the local football team. She thinks they're wonderful. The fact that she is sometimes the only person on the terrace does not worry her in the slightest. She is the stuff of which loyal fans are made and has been known to pay £1.50 on the bus to follow her heroes. We are talking dedicated here!

The Ed keeps her life outside of the office pretty quiet. I think she's worried one of us finds out her address, but we have managed to discover that she is the proud mum of two lovely cats — Cupcake and Fern. She's very fond of cats and is always coming into the office with another framed little picture of a kitten or a feline ornament. Speaking of which, ohh, ohh, here she comes now . . .

MOIRA

Everyone in the office keeps telling me that Moira has changed a lot over the last year. In fact, from what I can make out, she's gone from discoing three times a week to wall-papering and painting a flat. She still occasionally flits down to the disco, but she's more than likely to be talking about pine breadbins when you meet her. What has brought about this amazing transformation and, more to the point, is it catching?

It turns out that our Moira has always harboured a secret desire to live in her own little flat. Her mum and dad were only too pleased to see the back of her when she finally got the keys to Buckingham Palace . . . Em, sorry, I meant Arcadia Avenue, of course; it's just that listening to Moira you sometimes get confused which is which. Between her red kitchen and her pine furniture she really is the housewife extraordinaire.

The really amazing thing is that she's met a bloke who's exactly the same as she is. I mean, how else do you explain a boy buying her a pine breadbin two weeks after they'd met? Moira was totally over the moon about it (although I personally would have crowned him with it and asked where the flowers and choccies were). This boy, however, is made for our Moira and she is very happy to wander off into the sunset with him, clutching her pine breadbin under one arm . . .

Not that she ever puts anything in the pine breadbin. Moira is constantly on a diet and wouldn't dream of having bread in the house anyway.

the proud owner of a horse called Tanya and is continually taking her to shows and out for long rides, not to mention visits to the vet. In fact, I would say that Kerin spends more time looking after Tanya than she does herself, but anyone who knows her passion for a new haircut every two days would know that this isn't true.

Kerin is the only person I know who can arrive at work with a new hairstyle, get it cut into another one at lunchtime and then go again at 5 o'clock because she's decided she's bored with it already. The haircut has not been invented that this woman has not tried. She's not giving up the search, though. Kerin has subscriptions to every hairdressing magazine there is. One day she is going to find it — the perfect haircut!

In between haircuts Kerin is usually found with her nose buried in her black book. I would have said little black book but Kerin's book is huge, she needs the space to get all the names in. She hasn't exactly been the luckiest person in love, our Kerin, but all that will change one day and she wants to be ready for it when it does. She doesn't give up easily, certainly not until she's worked her way through her black book anyway!

Kerin likes going out to clubs and discos and she's also just recently discovered the joys of holidaying abroad. In fact, if you ever want any advice on a holiday (romance)

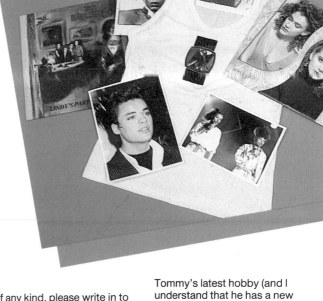

She lives on diet Coke and vitamin pills most of the time, although a few bran flakes have been known to pass her lips. She swears that her weight goes up and down by two stone at a time and has been known to utter the immortal words that she'll be the only walking skeleton with a big behind. The best laugh is that she looks just fine, but there's no point in telling her, she wouldn't believe you anyway.

KERIN

Kerin leads such a busy life it's a wonder she has time to come into work at all. She is

of any kind, please write in to her. She is now the office expert and could even pen you a love note or two in French with the practice she got from her last romantic encounter. What was his name again, Kerin? Bruno . . . ? Snigger . . . !

TOMMY

Tommy is our Pop Editor. If you want to know anything about the charts or who's who in pop, ask Tommy. Not that he's likely to tell you, it's just that he's supposed to know and sometimes we make the mistake of thinking that he does. In fact, as far as I can see, Tommy has the perfect job. He sits all day reading the music papers, listening to the free LPs that the record companies send him and trying on the free T-shirts . . . And that's just when he's at home! At work he does the exact same thing and gets paid for it.

One consolation is that all the T-shirts are usually too big. He's a bit on the very slim side is Tommy. Not that you'd think it if you saw the poor man groaning under the weight of all the empty Coke cans, crisp packets, fish 'n' chip wrappers, chocolate sweetie papers and everything else that's in his bin every day. Tommy's bin man has had to go on a weight-lifting course to cope!

Outside the office,

Tommy's latest hobby (and I understand that he has a new one every few weeks or so), is making films with a video camera. He's given up on being a pop star himself now and has decided to be a great film maker instead. Strange that he didn't look too keen on Moira's idea of doing a film giving a detailed tour of her new flat . . .

Tommy's quite a romantic on the quiet, although he would kill anyone who said so. There's even a rumour going round the office that he cut his girlfriend's grass last month, and for hip and trendy Tommy to do that it must be bad! I'm not being brave writing this about him, it's just that he's never read anything else that goes round the office and I doubt he's going to start now!

JUDEY

What can I say about Judey? Certainly nothing that hasn't been said before, that's for sure! Judey loves to wear skirts that are made out of one of her mum's old flannels, which gives you some idea of what length they are. Teamed up with black fishnet tights and multi-coloured hair, she has been known to turn a few heads or two — mainly men working on building sites who seem strangely compelled to shout at her.

This annoys our Judey no end and the men on the building sites are more often

annoying when you're enjoying a packet of crisps and she tells you it would've been 3 pence cheaper if you'd paid 40 pence on the bus and shopped somewhere else!

Cath is a great believer in keeping fit, too. She goes to aerobics or weight-training every lunchtime and horse-riding at night. Mind you, she never looks fit, she just looks

weighs less than three tons at any time. This is because she believes in carting every single thing she owns round with her all the time. It came as a great surprise to her recently that she'd pulled a muscle in her shoulder from carrying her bag and the doctor has now advised her to carry a rucksack instead. She hasn't actually discarded any of the stuff she carries, though — just transferred it to the rucksack!

When Kerin has finished with her hairdressing magazines she often passes them across to Ruth who is also searching for the ideal hairstyle. Ruth has been known to have her hair up, down and up again in between arriving at the office at 9 o'clock and the tea break at 10 o'clock! She is currently working on the theory that a perm would solve all her problems but hasn't seen the one that she likes yet . . .

Having inside information on what's happening in the fashion world sometimes gives Ruth an unfair advantage over the rest of us. Unfortunately for her, it usually means that she's wearing thick black leggings and a woollen overdress while the rest of us are wearing skimpy T-shirts and shorts, since fashion is always one season ahead. Today, for example, she's wearing a lovely pair of shorts that show her blue knees off to perfection — it's just a pity it's snowing outside when she looks so nice!

than not shocked by what she has said in reply. She's very independent, you see. Mind you, she's a complete pushover where animals are concerned. Judey has her own horse, Jonah, and a dog, Rags, she's had for 12 years. She's totally mad keen on just about every animal alive, and trying to get her to hurry up when she wants to pet every dog she passes is absolutely impossible!

She's also mad keen on Julian Cope and has made up her mind that she's going to get him one way or the other. Knowing Judey, the poor boy doesn't stand a chance — he'd be as well giving in now rather than exhausting himself

by struggling any further.

Judey is also a connoisseur of fairgrounds. She has a lot of friends who work for a travelling carnival and sometimes goes down to give them a hand when they're busy. She can make a mean candyfloss and name every single showboy between John O'Groats and Land's End. No doubt they'd be able to name her too, but that's another story and I quite like working here!

CATH

Cath is the poor soul who does the Help! page in the weekly magazine. I say poor soul because we hardly ever get to see her — her desk is usually piled so high with letters from readers. Cath likes her job, she's quite cheerful and friendly by nature and doesn't seem to let other people's problems get her down. She gets a bit annoyed when everyone in the office treats her as their personal Agony Aunt, though. No wonder she sits with her personal Hi-Fi and headphones on all day. So would I if I were her . . .

If you ever want to know where the cheapest tin of beans or pound of plums is in the whole town, ask Cath. She has a photographic memory for details such as the price of groceries and has been known to recite entire shopping lists to prove her point. It gets a bit

exhausted from keeping fit! And it's a bit disconcerting when you open the filing cabinet looking for something and her gym shoes are staring up at you. Mind you, it was even worse when she used to hang her swimsuit out to dry on the radiator. All afternoon we were treated to the fragrant aroma of chlorine . . . Ugh!

RUTH

Ruth is our Fashion Editor and she's the one responsible for no-one being able to find their desks because she's got clothes lying everywhere ready for a photographic session. She's also the one who's on the phone every week tearing her hair out because the model she wanted to book has gone to Japan again or run away to Outer Mongolia. Even worse is when the model she books shows up and looks completely different from the photos she's been sent.

Ruth is also renowned for never carrying a bag that

SHOWER POWER!

Feeling slightly sleepy and can't find your way to the bathroom door because your eyes refuse to open? Crawling home after a hard day, grumpy, hot and a bit rough around the edges? Throw yourself in the shower and emerge fresh, revitalised, tingling and ready to go!

Before stepping into the shower, ensure you have all the odds and ends you need: i.e. shampoo, conditioner, a wide toothed comb for combing the conditioner through, towels, gels, razors, kitchen sink, cuddly toy etc., etc., etc.!

Turn the water on full, making sure it's not too hot (you don't want to come out like a boiled shrivelled beetroot), and let the force of the water stimulate your circulation.

Cast aside your old bar of coal tar and treat yourself to a soap on a rope, or liquid soap which you simply squeeze onto a flannel or natural sponge (the Body Shop do particularly nice ones). Shower gels and body shampoos, too, are a good alternative to soap. Squirt the gel or shampoo straight onto your body, then use a flannel or sponge to work up a good lather to leave your skin soft and smelling fresh.

While you're in the shower take the opportunity to slough off any dead skin cells. A loofah mitt is the ideal answer to this, but if money's tight, just moisten a handful of coarse sea salt (available from most health food shops) and rub it all over your body. Rinse off and feel the difference!

You may think that pumice stones are only for your gran's bunions and corns, but they're excellent for smoothing away hard skin on the heels and soles of your feet — you can usually pick up a good one for around £1.50.

When you finally raise your head above the water, step out of the shower, rub yourself dry with a soft warm towel (bliss!), and massage in some baby lotion.

Finally, spray yourself with your favourite deodorising body spray for day-long freshness!

TELLY HUNK

Phillip Schofield

TELLY HUNK
Nick Berry

"D'YOU think it's gonna snow?" John glanced up at the heavy grey sky hopefully. "It's been really cold all day."

"Yeah." I pushed my hands deeper into the pockets of my long black coat. That was the problem with trying to be trendy — you were always freezing, especially in weather like this. Mum had tried to make me wear a duffle coat — I mean I ask you! Better to freeze than look like a nerd, I'd told her — but I reckoned it wouldn't take much to change my mind.

"I actually thought we were gonna get sent home," John went on, kicking a Coke can out of his way. "It was brassers in German — I was hoping the pipes had frozen."

In all the time I'd been going out with John he never ceased to amaze me. I thought I knew him but there was always something new to find out about him. Like this past week. It was the week before Christmas, and John had never shut up about snow. It seems it's his lifelong dream to have a white Christmas. He says he wants to build snowmen in the park on Christmas morning. Personally I'd rather open the pressies and get torn in about my little sister's selection box, but there you are.

The streets were full of Christmas shoppers. Women were hobbling along, weighed down with Tesco carrier bags with triple packs of wrapping paper sticking out of the top. Taxis were doing a roaring trade, and you couldn't move for squalling kids.

"I think children should be banned at Christmas," I remarked. "In the shops, anyway."

"Yeah." John wasn't really listening. He was miles away, as usual. Alaska, probably.

We had to walk through the shopping centre to get home, and as we passed H. Samuel's I spotted the chain I'd planned to buy for John.

"Is there anything you specially want for Christmas?" I asked him. "Before I go and splash out my life-savings on something else?"

John grinned. "I have great faith in your wonderful taste, Cathy," he said modestly. He meant I had great taste because I was going out with him.

DRESS YOU UP

A Patches Short Story

He was right, though. You should see him. To say Tom Cruise doesn't have a look in might be over-stating the matter slightly, but he's certainly the best-looking non-megastar you're ever likely to see. He's got this dark, dark brown hair — it's almost black, in fact — and big, light brown eyes. I think he's lovely, but what he's doing with me is of course another matter. I look very ordinary. In fact, I'm so ordinary it's quite depressing and I don't even want to talk about it.

We walked on, slowly, through the masses, and we got held up in a people jam just outside Top Shop. I glanced in the window — and there and then, after years of hating and taking the mickey, I became a Top Shop convert on the spot.

"Look at that dress!" I squeaked. It was beautiful. It was long and black and made of patterned, velvety stuff. It had a V down the front (and the back, although I didn't know it then) and it hadn't any sleeves.

It was the most gorgeous dress I'd ever seen, and I would have sold anything to get it. Even John. I could easily find another boyfriend wearing that. Unfortunately, it was about thirty quid.

"Cathy, that's a horrible dress," John said, surprised. "You wouldn't buy that, would you?"

"I'd sell anything to get it," I declared, omitting to mention that that included him.

"Blimey," he said in disgust, and we carried on walking.

*   *   *

Things started to go wrong after that. After he'd accidentally forgotten to tell me (for the third night in a row) that he had to stay behind at school, and had left me freezing to death at the gate for half an hour, I really started to worry. And every time I got upset, I would go and look at the dress. And every time I saw the dress, something else awful happened.

"That dress is a jinx," I said to my sister Fiona on Friday night. John had just phoned to say sorry, he couldn't come round tonight because he was too tired. "Too tired indeed. He wasn't too tired to go out with his horrible mates last night!"

"It's not the dress, Cathy," Fiona said. "That's stupid. It just looks like John's cooling off. But I must say, if he

was going to finish with you he might at least have the courage to tell you to your face."

She was talking as if we were finished already. "John's not going to finish with me!" I yelled. "He's been going out with me for a year now."

"So?" Fiona raised her eyes briefly from Cosmo. "Marriages of twenty years standing can break up, Catherine — one year is hardly any time at all."

"Well thanks for nothing," I muttered. But she'd started me thinking now. Before, I'd only been worried that he was cross with me about something. It had honestly never entered my head that he might not want to see me any more.

The phone rang then, interrupting my thoughts. It was Jenny, my best mate.

"Just checking we're still doing our shopping tomorrow," she said, so casually that I knew she was lying.

"And what else?" I said.

"Oh, Cath — I really don't like to tell you this . . ."

"But I get the feeling you're going to anyway," I interrupted. "Go on. What is it? Has someone bought my dress?"

"No, it's worse than that. I just saw John going into Sally's house."

Sally Robinson lived across the road from Jenny. Sally Robinson was small, blonde and pretty. And cute.

And witty. I'd liked her all my life. Until now. But the first thing that sprung into my mind was not that she was a cow for pinching my boyfriend, nor that John was a dirty two-timing pig, but that I'd only to mention the dress and something dire happened. It was beginning to get scary.

". . . and so near to Christmas, too," Jenny was saying. "What a rotten thing to do."

I hung up. Suddenly I couldn't stand it. John and I were forever — he couldn't be going out with Sally. I'd punch her face. No, I'd punch his face. What a coward. Couldn't even tell me like a man. I felt sick, and I wished I'd never set eyes on that horrible jinxed dress.

Fiona spotted me in floods of tears, and with the insight and Sherlockian sharpness I've come to expect from her, she deduced I was upset.

"I'm going to phone him up and tell him to get knotted," I gulped between howls.

"Oh no you're not," Fiona said, with surprising spirit. "You're going to wait until he has the guts to tell you himself. Don't give him an easy way out. Make him face up to his responsibilities."

She made it sound like I was pregnant or something.

Continued on page 38

C

That's What Friends Are For...

KIRSTY SOUNDED DESPERATE ON THE PHONE, AND THAT USUALLY MEANS ONE THING — BOY TROUBLE! WHY DOES SHE ALWAYS PICK SUCH CREEPS? SHE JUST GETS HURT.

And so . . .

OH, IT WAS AWFUL, SANDRA . . . HE SAID HE'D FOUND SOMEONE ELSE AND HE DIDN'T WANT TO SEE ME AGAIN. JUST LIKE THAT. I DIDN'T GET A CHANCE TO SAY ANYTHING.

LUCKY YOU WEREN'T WITH COLIN WHEN I PHONED. I REALLY NEEDED SOMEONE TO TALK TO.

OH, DON'T WORRY, I'D STILL HAVE COME OVER. COLIN WOULD'VE UNDERSTOOD.

TH-THANKS FOR COMING, ANYWAY. I DON'T KNOW WHAT I'D DO WITHOUT YOU. I ALWAYS SEEM TO BE GETTING DUMPED BY SOME ROTTEN CREEP OR OTHER.

POOR KIRSTY. WHY CAN'T SHE PICK SOMEONE NICE FOR A CHANGE? LIKE MY COLIN. BUT SHE ALWAYS ENDS UP WITH SOME TWO-TIMING RAT.

C'MON, I RECOMMEND A WALK IN THE PARK FOLLOWED BY COFFEE AND A HUGE, STICKY CREAM CAKE. BEST THING FOR CURING A BROKEN HEART.

Later . . .

IT STILL HURTS WHEN I THINK ABOUT HIM, SANDRA, BUT I'M FEELING A BIT BETTER NOW. THANKS FOR CHEERING ME UP.

LOOK, KIRSTY . . . YOU PROBABLY WON'T LIKE ME FOR SAYING THIS, BUT WHY DO YOU GET INVOLVED WITH SUCH CREEPS? YOU FALL IN LOVE WITH THEM IN TWO WEEKS FLAT, BEFORE YOU'VE EVEN FOUND OUT WHAT THEY'RE REALLY LIKE.

I KNOW — AND IT WON'T HAPPEN AGAIN. I'M NOT GOING OUT ANY MORE.

THAT WON'T SOLVE ANYTHING! DO YOU REALLY SEE YOURSELF AS A HERMIT?

NO, BUT IT'S EASY FOR YOU, SANDRA — YOU'VE GOT COLIN.

P A T C H E S

YES, AND WE'RE GOING OUT FOR A MEAL TOMORROW NIGHT. WHY NOT JOIN US?

EM . . . I'M NOT SURE. IT WOULDN'T BE RIGHT . . . WELL, NOT UNLESS YOU ASKED COLIN FIRST . . .

But that evening, as Colin waited for Sandra . . .

HI! ARE YOU NEW HERE? I HAVEN'T SEEN YOU BEFORE.

THAT'S BECAUSE I ONLY STARTED THIS WEEK.

MM . . . SHE'S NOT BAD. I'LL HAVE TO COME HERE MORE OFTEN — WITHOUT SANDRA!

When Sandra arrived . . .

COLIN! WAKE UP—YOU'RE MILES AWAY.

OH — SORRY SANDRA. I DIDN'T SEE YOU COME IN. I WAS JUST ER . . . WONDERING WHETHER TO HAVE ANOTHER COKE. I'VE BEEN WAITING AGES.

YEAH, I'M SORRY. I HOPE YOU DIDN'T MIND WAITING. KIRSTY'S HAVING PROBLEMS AGAIN.

WHY SHOULD I MIND — I'VE BEEN ENJOYING THE SCENERY!

OH, DEAR— SO, WHAT'S SHE BEEN UP TO THIS TIME?

OH, THE USUAL. SHE ATTACHED HERSELF TO ANOTHER NO-HOPER, HE DITCHED HER, AND NOW SHE'S ALL UPSET.

SO I . . . EM . . . HOPE YOU DON'T MIND, BUT I INVITED HER OUT WITH US TOMORROW NIGHT.

THAT'S OK. ANYTHING TO HELP A FRIEND.

THANKS. I KNEW YOU WOULDN'T MIND, COLIN. YOU'RE GREAT.

The following evening . . .

THIS IS REALLY GOOD OF YOU, COLIN. ARE YOU SURE YOU DON'T MIND?

NOT AT ALL. WE WANT YOU TO ENJOY YOURSELF — OR YOU'LL BE PAYING FOR THE MEAL! NOW, WOULD YOU LADIES LIKE A DRINK BEFORE WE DINE . . .

P A T C H E S

THAT WAS NICE OF COLIN TO DROP BY. MAYBE HE'S RIGHT ABOUT THE DISCO. KAREN AND ANGELA AND THAT LOT USUALLY GO ON FRIDAYS. I MIGHT MEET SOME OF THEM UP THERE.

But on Friday . . .

THIS IS AWFUL. THERE'S NOT A SOUL HERE I KNOW. I MIGHT AS WELL GO HOME . . .

But then . . .

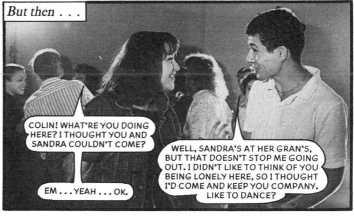

COLIN! WHAT'RE YOU DOING HERE? I THOUGHT YOU AND SANDRA COULDN'T COME?

EM . . . YEAH . . . OK.

WELL, SANDRA'S AT HER GRAN'S, BUT THAT DOESN'T STOP ME GOING OUT. I DIDN'T LIKE TO THINK OF YOU BEING LONELY HERE, SO I THOUGHT I'D COME AND KEEP YOU COMPANY. LIKE TO DANCE?

They spent the evening together . . .

. . . AND THERE HE WAS, TRYING TO IMPRESS THIS GIRL, WHEN HE TRIPPED HEAD FIRST OVER HER DOG!

OH, COLIN, YOU'VE REALLY CHEERED ME UP. I HAVEN'T ENJOYED MYSELF SO MUCH FOR AGES.

Later . . .

IT'S A SHAME I'VE GOT TO GO HOME NOW. I'VE HAD A GREAT TIME TONIGHT.

WELL, THERE ARE PLENTY OTHER NIGHTS.

HOW D'YOU MEAN . . . ?

I MEAN, WE CAN GO OUT AGAIN — WITHOUT SANDRA.

NO, COLIN! SANDRA'S MY BEST FRIEND.

WHAT DOES IT MATTER? C'MON, SANDRA'LL NEVER KNOW.

KIRSTY— COME BACK! AT LEAST THINK ABOUT IT!

OH, NO! WHAT HAVE I DONE? I SHOULDN'T HAVE STAYED AT THE DISCO. I SHOULD'VE REALISED . . . IF I GO OUT WITH COLIN, SANDRA'LL NEVER SPEAK TO ME AGAIN.

P A T C H E S

continued on page 42

DRESS YOU UP

Continued from page 33

So until John told me we were finished, we were still a couple. Fine. I kept well out of his way so that he couldn't tell me. If I saw him coming along the corridor at school, I dodged into the nearest classroom and hid in a cupboard. If he phoned, I was out. If I saw him in the street, I ran away.

About three days from Christmas, I decided things were getting out of hand. I was going mad — running away from John and rushing past Top Shop because I was frightened to look at my dress. That was nonsense.

"OK, Cathy," I said to myself. "You are going into Top Shop, and you are going to try on that dress, and then you are going round to see John and ask him what is going on."

I stomped into Top Shop, grabbed an assistant and made her get the dress for me, I took it into the changing room and tried it on, and I fell in love with it all over again. Honestly, it was so gorgeous it even made me look great. It made me look taller, prettier, thinner . . . I wanted that dress more than anything in the world — except John.

Reluctantly I took it off and gave it back to the girl outside the changing room. "No use?" she said.

"Lots of use," I replied, "no money."

The girl laughed and hung up my beloved dress with all the other rejected garments. I walked out of the shop feeling better, and if you'll believe me, the first thing I saw was John walking towards me with Sally Robinson. I nearly died.

"Cathy!" John shouted. I screamed and ran away.

I spent the most miserable night of my life the day before Christmas Eve. I cried solidly through "The Two Ronnies Christmas Extravaganza", "The Wizard Of Oz" and "Billy Smart's Circus". I just couldn't imagine life without John, and what hurt most was that he'd gone behind my back and hadn't even had enough consideration for my feelings to tell me straight out.

Then on Christmas Eve, I was sitting up in my bedroom listening to a Lionel Richie tape and snivelling miserably. I'd run out of tears by that time. Suddenly there was a knock on my bedroom door.

"What?"

"It's Santa!"

It wasn't — it was John.

"How did you get in?" I demanded. "I didn't hear the doorbell."

"Met Fiona in the street. Hey, what's wrong?"

I nearly exploded, "What's wrong? *You're* wrong! You and Sally Robinson are wrong! I've not seen you for about two weeks, and then I spot you with her in the town, and you ask me what's wrong? You don't even have the decency to . . ."

"Cathy," John said calmly, "shut your face."

I shut it.

"Look, there's nothing going on between Sally and me," he told me. "Honestly. The last thing on my mind is finishing with you, and even if I wanted to, I'd tell you to your face."

"Well, that's what I thought," I mumbled, "but . . ."

John sighed. "Look, I came round with your present for tomorrow, but I think you'd better have it tonight. Then you'll see where Sally came into all this."

He took a parcel from behind his back, wrapped in purple tissue paper.

"You see, I knew how much you liked that hideous dress, so I thought I'd buy it for you. Only I didn't know what size you were, so I asked Sally to try it on — I knew the two of you are about the same."

A great wave of relief washed over me. And strangely enough, it wasn't the fact that John and I were still together that pleased me most. I was just glad my dress hadn't turned out to be a jinx after all.

"Can I open it now?"

He nodded, and I tore the paper off. And gulped. It wasn't my beautiful black dress that was lying on the bed — it was a short, tarty red affair. I gaped.

"Happy?"

"Well — yeah — I mean — yeah."

"Try it on, then."

Oh God. It was all coming back to me now. I had a vague recollection of a red article on a model beside my dress in the window. No wonder John had said it was hideous. He was right.

John turned his back discreetly, and I hauled off my jeans and jersey and slipped the dress over my head and fluffed up my hair a bit. I couldn't bear to look in the mirror.

John turned round. "Wow! Well, I apologise for doubting your impeccable taste, Cathy — it looks great!"

Apprehensively I glanced in the mirror. He was right, as well — it was a terrific dress. So we kissed and made up, and everything was just great, and John need never have known he'd made a mistake, but for Fiona.

"Just coming in for a look at the dress," she called, barging in before I could stop her. "Oh — but that's not the one you showed me, Cathy — it was black, wasn't it?"

So then it all came out. John apologised a million times and I said it was OK, I loved this one, but in the end we got it all sorted out. John says I can take the dress back after Boxing Day and exchange it for the other one. I suppose I could, but I don't think I will — I don't think I'm that keen on it now, anyway.

THE END.

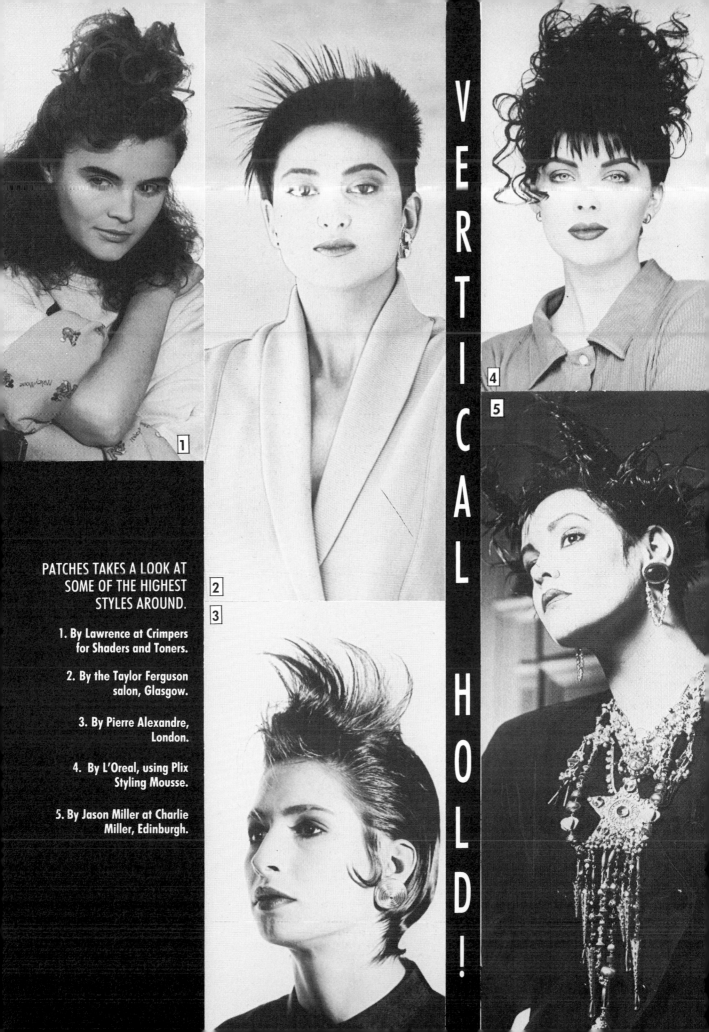

VERTICAL HOLD!

PATCHES TAKES A LOOK AT SOME OF THE HIGHEST STYLES AROUND.

1. By Lawrence at Crimpers for Shaders and Toners.

2. By the Taylor Ferguson salon, Glasgow.

3. By Pierre Alexandre, London.

4. By L'Oreal, using Plix Styling Mousse.

5. By Jason Miller at Charlie Miller, Edinburgh.

liggin', giggin' and

"She thinks if she covers her eyes then she'll become more mysterious!" Bananarama discuss their tactics for facing our photographers . . .

George Michael loiters around a (not-very-busy) London street corner waiting to see if anyone will recognise him . . .
Why not try 'A Different Corner', George? (har . . . !)

Pop's little pearl, Pete Burns, hides away in an oyster shell . . .

Ole-greasy-pork-sausage-features, Freddie Mercury, lets his teeth and belly all hang out while getting sporty . . . Anyone for tennis? Anyone for a strict diet?

Andrew Ridgeley and girlfriend Donya both put on their shades during a huffy moment.

posin'

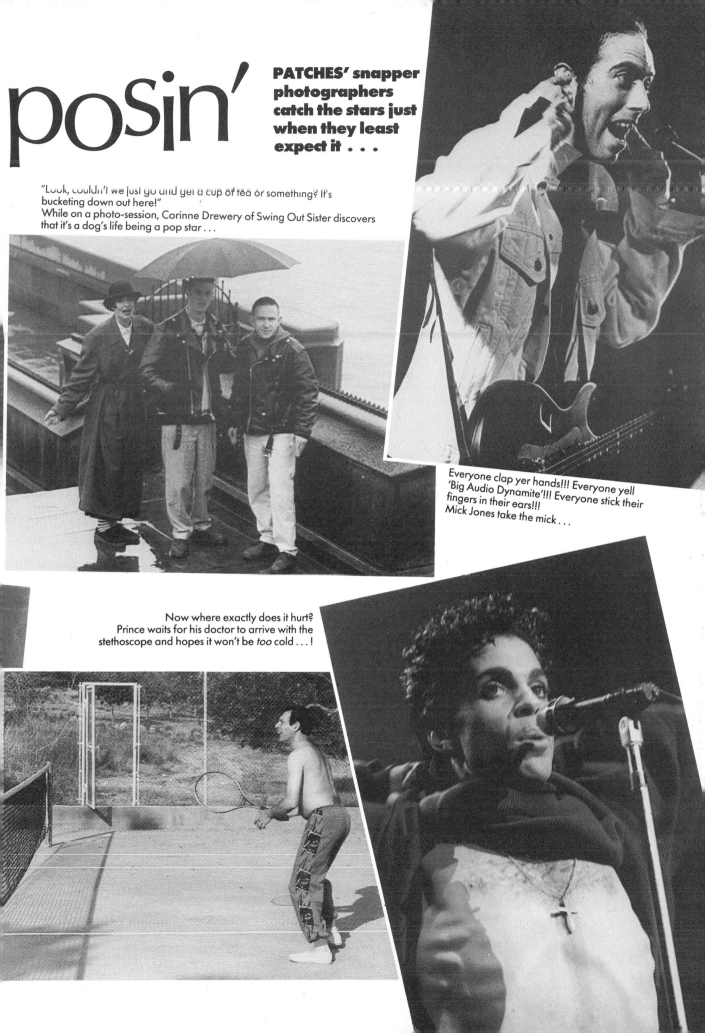

"Look, couldn't we just go and get a cup of tea or something? It's bucketing down out here!"
While on a photo-session, Corinne Drewery of Swing Out Sister discovers that it's a dog's life being a pop star . . .

Everyone clap yer hands!!! Everyone yell 'Big Audio Dynamite'!!! Everyone stick their fingers in their ears!!!
Mick Jones take the mick . . .

Now where exactly does it hurt?
Prince waits for his doctor to arrive with the stethoscope and hopes it won't be *too* cold . . . !

That's What Friends Are For...

The next morning . . .

I DON'T KNOW WHAT TO DO. I SHOULD JUST TELL COLIN TO GET LOST, BUT . . . WELL . . . I QUITE FANCY HIM REALLY. HE'S NOT THE BORING PERSON I THOUGHT HE WAS.

ON THE OTHER HAND, SANDRA'S COMING ROUND TONIGHT. MAYBE I SHOULD TELL HER WHAT COLIN'S REALLY LIKE.

But that evening . . .

C-COLIN!

DON'T LOOK SO SURPRISED. I KNOW SANDRA'S COMING AT SEVEN, SO I'VE ARRIVED EARLY. WELL, INVITE ME IN — OR I'LL KISS YOU RIGHT HERE ON THE DOORSTEP!

COLIN, PLEASE, DON'T MESS ABOUT. I HAVEN'T DECIDED TO GO OUT WITH YOU YET.

OH, THAT DOESN'T MATTER. YOU AND SANDRA ARE BEST FRIENDS SO WE'LL BE SEEING PLENTY OF EACH OTHER. SOONER OR LATER YOU'LL AGREE. IN THE MEANTIME, I CAN WAIT.

Kirsty was relieved when Sandra arrived . . .

OH, GOOD, YOU'RE HERE ALREADY COLIN. IT MUST BE YOUR GOOD INFLUENCE, KIRSTY. COLIN NEVER USUALLY ARRIVES EARLY.

I MUST GET SANDRA ON HER OWN AND TELL HER WHAT COLIN'S BEEN UP TO . . .

And so, later . . .

I-I'VE GOT SOMETHING TO TELL YOU, SANDRA — ABOUT COLIN.

OH YEAH? WHAT?

WELL . . . I . . .

IT'S NO USE. I CAN'T TELL HER. I HAVEN'T GOT THE COURAGE. I'M NOT SURE SHE'D BELIEVE ME, ANYWAY, AND IF SHE DID, SHE'D BE REALLY UPSET.

OH, SANDRA, IT'S JUST . . . I CAN'T BELIEVE HOW GOOD HE'S BEEN IN HELPING ME. WELL, BOTH OF YOU, ACTUALLY. I'M REALLY GRATEFUL.

IS THAT ALL? I THOUGHT IT WAS GOING TO BE SOMETHING REALLY BAD THE WAY YOU WERE TALKING. WE DON'T MIND HELPING. YOU ARE MY BEST FRIEND, AFTER ALL.

Colin didn't give up trying . . .

MMM, THEY'RE LOVELY. I'VE NEVER HAD FLOWERS BEFORE, AND I BET I CAN GUESS WHO SENT THEM. WHAT DOES THE NOTE SAY? "WITH ALL MY LOVE". OH, COLIN, IT WOULD BE SO EASY TO GO OUT WITH YOU. BUT I CAN'T. I MUSTN'T . . .

The next morning . . .

WELL, AREN'T YOU GOING TO THANK ME FOR THE FLOWERS?

YES, THEY'RE LOVELY. THANKS COLIN. I-I'LL HAVE TO GO NOW OR I'LL BE LATE FOR WORK.

OK, BUT WHAT ABOUT TONIGHT . . . ?

And that afternoon . . .

AND AS I WAS SAYING BEFORE WORK INTERRUPTED OUR CONVERSATION — ANY CHANCE OF A DATE TONIGHT?

COLIN, HONESTLY, HOW LONG HAVE YOU BEEN WAITING? LOOK, I'VE TOLD YOU BEFORE, I CAN ONLY SEE YOU IF SANDRA IS WITH US.

P A T C H E S

At the party, the following evening . . .

HI, KIRSTY. HOW ABOUT THE FIRST DANCE?

WON'T SANDRA MIND?

'COURSE NOT. SHE'S BUSY OPENING PRESENTS. BESIDES, SHE TRUSTS ME, REMEMBER?

PHEW, THOSE PRESENTS TOOK A LONG TIME. I HAVEN'T HAD MUCH CHANCE TO BE WITH COLIN. STILL, HE'S BEEN DANCING WITH KIRSTY MOST OF THE EVENING. HE'S REALLY GOOD THAT WAY — ALWAYS HELPING TO CHEER HER UP.

But later . . .

WHERE'S COLIN GOT TO? I WANT HIM TO HELP ME GET SOME MORE FOOD AND STUFF IN. AND KIRSTY'S DISAPPEARED TOO . . . THAT'S ODD. I'D BETTER GO AND LOOK FOR THEM.

And . . .

NO, COLIN, PLEASE. LET ME GO. I MEAN IT THIS TIME. IT'S OVER. I CAN'T SEE YOU ANYMORE. I — I FEEL GUILTY, THINKING OF SANDRA.

OH NO! KIRSTY AND COLIN . . . I — I NEVER IMAGINED . . .

DON'T BE SO DAFT, KIRSTY. I'VE TOLD YOU BEFORE, WHAT SANDRA DOESN'T KNOW, WON'T HURT HER.

SANDRA! I CAN EXPLAIN . . .

REALLY? WELL, I THINK I CAN SEE CLEARLY ENOUGH MYSELF! GET OUT — BOTH OF YOU! YOU'RE WELCOME TO EACH OTHER!

TO THINK I TRUSTED COLIN . . . THOUGHT HE WAS JUST BEING KIND TO KIRSTY . . .

STILL, KIRSTY LIVED UP TO HER REPUTATION — SHE CAN ALWAYS PICK THE CREEPS. I SUPPOSE I SHOULD BE GRATEFUL. SHE SHOWED ME WHAT A RAT COLIN REALLY IS.

Later . . .

HOW COULD I HAVE BEEN SO STUPID? I LOVED HIM. I THOUGHT HE WAS THE PERFECT BOYFRIEND. NOW I'VE GOT TO TAKE SOME OF THE ADVICE I USUALLY GIVE KIRSTY AND TRY TO FORGET THE ROTTEN, TWO-TIMING CREEP . . .

And next morning . . .

I MIGHT'VE LOST A WORTHLESS BOYFRIEND, BUT ONE PERSON I CAN'T AFFORD TO LOSE RIGHT NOW IS MY BEST FRIEND. WHATEVER SHE'S DONE. IT'S TIME I GAVE KIRSTY A CALL . . .

THE END

P A T C H E S

CURIOSITY • KILLED • THE • CAT

Does the idea of weeding the garden seem attractive? Has cleaning out your room taken on Is clipping the dog's toenails the highlight of your week? Then it sounds like you could be terminal boredom. And being bored is, let's face it . . . boring. But fear no more! Follow and you'll soon wish there were more days in the week!

We all know the feeling — your eyes glaze over as you watch an endless round of dumbo quiz programmes, "Songs Of Praise" and "Gardener's World", you're on your fourth cup of tea and you've nibbled your way through an entire packet of digestive biscuits. "What happened to all the parties, discos and hunky guys with armfuls of red roses and big sports cars?" you ask yourself. Well, rest assured, we all have a boring day once in a while. But if you find yourself feeling bored, depressed and down in the dumps most of the time, maybe it's time you took a closer look at your life.

Bored because you've nothing to do?

Well, what's required here is a bit of effort. Have you thought about taking up a sport or a new hobby? Don't all groan at once — sport doesn't have to mean goosepimpled school girls in bum-freezing games' skirts charging about on an ice-cold hockey pitch. As well as the more common sports such as tennis, badminton, athletics, swimming etc., most large towns cater for more exotic pursuits like volleyball, ladies football, weight training, fencing and so on. Your local library, sports centre or sports shop will be able to provide you with a list of all the various clubs in your area. As well as keeping fit, you'll probably find yourself making a few new friends, too.

The mere thought of exercise turns you into a pale, quivering wreck? Well, don't despair, there's still plenty to keep the more lethargic amongst us occupied.

During the autumn and winter, most schools and community centres run evening classes. The entrance fee for under-18s is usually quite cheap, so why not drag a friend along and learn to throw pots, paint masterpieces or even mend the car?!

If organised activities don't appeal to you, why not dig the sewing machine out of the cupboard and make yourself some clothes, learn to play a musical instrument (who knows where the path to pop stardom starts?) or even try to find a part-time job?

Bored with your boyfriend?

Fed up sitting in night after night watching TV or going to the same old places and meeting the same old people? Maybe you and your boyfriend have just got into a rut and by making a conscious effort to change your routine you can revive your relationship.

On the other hand, perhaps it's your boyfriend himself you're bored with? If this is the case, you'll just have to face up to the fact that it may be time to finish your relationship.

When you first go out with someone, life seems exciting — you've a lot to learn about each other, stories and experiences to swap. But once you know someone inside-out, it's quite easy for Mr Wonderful to turn into Mr Mega-Bore 1988.

Whatever you do, don't stay in a dead relationship just for the sake of it. Being able to say, "I've got a boyfriend" isn't worth being bored out of your skull every

Don't Just Sit There

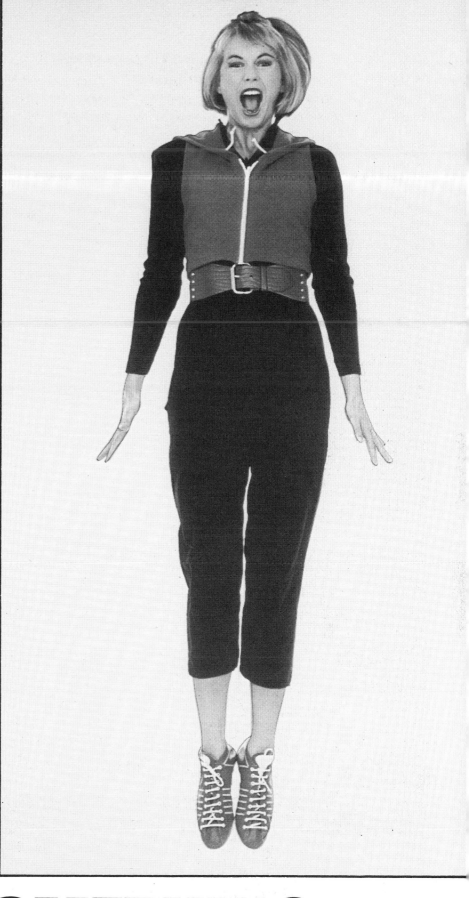

Saturday night. And remember, being tied up with someone you don't like is keeping you from meeting other boys who might be ten times more interesting.

Bored with school?

Well, it would be a rare person indeed who found school interesting all the time. When you're taking between seven and ten different subjects a week, you can hardly be expected to find them *all* deeply interesting. But when you think about it, there must be something you enjoy.

How about Art, or maybe you enjoy P.E. when you get to stay inside and play volleyball or basketball? We bet there's at least one of your teachers you like and who's a good laugh sometimes. And how about all the time you spend gossiping with your mates or eyeing up the fifth years running up and down the football pitch in their natty little shorts?

Like everything else, school has its good bits and its bad bits. Try to concentrate on the good things, though, rather than constantly depressing yourself with thoughts of Geography with boring Mr Pearson or that History test next week. It'll make you a much more pleasant person to know.

Do you find yourself plunged into the depths of boredom and despair every so often for no apparent reason?

This could well be linked to your periods. Keep a note of the days you feel like this, and if they fall into a monthly pattern you may be suffering from pre-menstrual tension. P.M.T. has quite a few symptoms, but the most common include moodiness, depression and a general feeling of lethargy.

There isn't a lot you can do about this, but if your family or friends are worried about your moods, it's best to explain things to them. Of course, if you start to feel extremely depressed, it's advisable to consult your doctor who may be able to give you something to help.

So next time, before you cry "I'm bored!" and drive your family away screaming, think if there's a reason for it and if there's anything at all you can possibly do about it. After all, there's always the dusting or the hoovering or the ironing or . . . on second thoughts, perhaps "Songs Of Praise" isn't such a bad idea . . .

—DO SOMETHING!

LABOUR OF LOVE

I'd split up with my boyfriend three weeks ago, and since then my mate had spent all her time matchmaking. I was fed up with it. Why couldn't she just leave me alone to be miserable?

"What are you doing tonight then, Wendy?" was the first thing Susan said to me when I picked up the phone.

"Staying in," I told her slowly, clearly, and threateningly.

"That's a shame. You see, I thought we could..."

"No."

"But, Wend, I've just been talking to..."

"No."

"And she knows this sexy guy who..."

"No!"

"Oh, all right then. Be like that. See you on Monday," and Susan rang off perfectly cheerfully.

I stomped back into the living-room and released the pause button on the video.

"Who was that?" my brother asked as I sat down.

"It was Susan, matchmaking again."

Tom laughed. "She's only trying to help. She doesn't want you to sit about moping over Colin."

"I never get the flaming chance," I snorted. It was true too. Since Colin and I had split up, Sue had spent all her time trying to pair me off with someone new.

"Won't do you any good brooding over him," she kept telling me. The way she carried on you'd think I was suicidal or something — all I wanted was a couple of weeks to be miserable — you're entitled to that when you've just been packed in. But could Sue see that? You must be joking!

Two nights after we'd broken up, Sue had been on the phone. "Come out with me tonight, Wendy. Bruce is away tonight and I told my cousin we could go out..."

Of course, her cousin was a boy. Paul, his name was. He wasn't bad-looking, but tedious doesn't begin to describe his conversation. We left earlier than was strictly polite, but Susan wasn't discouraged.

"Never mind, Wend," she'd said, patting my shoulder consolingly, "he was a long shot anyway. What are you doing tomorrow...?"

And to cut a long story short, it was still going on. It wasn't that I didn't appreciate her being worried about me and all that — I mean it would have been OK if she had an ounce of taste. Would you go out with a Meatloaf lookalike called Beastie? Or a milky bar kid clone? I rest my case.

"So she's had it," I told Tom. "Beastie was positively her last chance ever. I'm staying in tonight to watch 'Love Story' and mourn the loss of my wonderful boyfriend."

Tom laughed and said it was a wonder I could remember what Colin looked like after all the boys I'd been out with over the past fortnight.

A Reader's True Story

But I could remember Colin all right. More importantly, I could remember the night we split up.

"Look, Wendy, I'm sorry," he'd said flatly, "but I really fancy Stacey and I'm going to ask her out. So it's best if we finish before I do."

I suppose it was nice of him to be so honest, but I didn't see it that way at the time. And the worst thing was that Stacey wasn't interested, so he asked Leah out instead. To think he could prefer Leah to me! I was nearly crying just thinking about it.

Tom noticed I was getting upset, and tactfully removed himself from the living room. Colin got on really well with Tom. They used to go to football matches together... For some reason that started me crying. Maybe Sue had the right idea after all. Maybe she knew how much I missed Colin.

I'd been snivelling for about fifteen minutes when I heard the phone ringing again. I reached for another tissue and ignored it. Two minutes later, Tom came into the living room and sat down. "That was Diane," he told me.

"So?"

"Well, she was wondering if you would do her a favour."

Continued on page 52

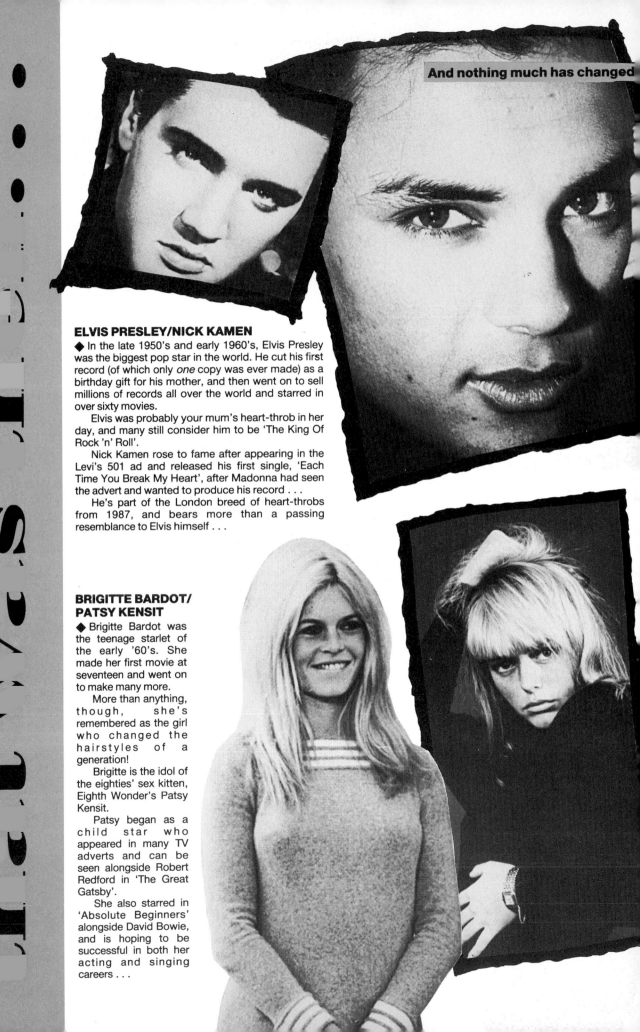

ELVIS PRESLEY/NICK KAMEN

◆ In the late 1950's and early 1960's, Elvis Presley was the biggest pop star in the world. He cut his first record (of which only *one* copy was ever made) as a birthday gift for his mother, and then went on to sell millions of records all over the world and starred in over sixty movies.

Elvis was probably your mum's heart-throb in her day, and many still consider him to be 'The King Of Rock 'n' Roll'.

Nick Kamen rose to fame after appearing in the Levi's 501 ad and released his first single, 'Each Time You Break My Heart', after Madonna had seen the advert and wanted to produce his record . . .

He's part of the London breed of heart-throbs from 1987, and bears more than a passing resemblance to Elvis himself . . .

BRIGITTE BARDOT/ PATSY KENSIT

◆ Brigitte Bardot was the teenage starlet of the early '60's. She made her first movie at seventeen and went on to make many more.

More than anything, though, she's remembered as the girl who changed the hairstyles of a generation!

Brigitte is the idol of the eighties' sex kitten, Eighth Wonder's Patsy Kensit.

Patsy began as a child star who appeared in many TV adverts and can be seen alongside Robert Redford in 'The Great Gatsby'.

She also starred in 'Absolute Beginners' alongside David Bowie, and is hoping to be successful in both her acting and singing careers . . .

but this is NOW?

JAMES DEAN/MATT DILLON

◆ A star of the early fifties who's since become a legend, is James Dean. He emerged in a film called 'Rebel Without A Cause', and then went on to make 'East Of Eden' and 'Giant'. With only three films under his belt, he died in a car crash while only in his twenties . . .

He's still a hero of the masses, and to this day many a James Dean lookalike can still be spotted in London.

Matt Dillon is the eighties equivalent of James Dean. A 'Rebel Without A Cause' himself, Matt led a life of crime on the streets before landing his first film part in 'The Outsiders'. He's gone on to star in 'RumbleFish' and 'The Flamingo Kid' and is a member of The Brat Pack — America's group of young heart-throb actors . . .

MICK JAGGER/ MICK JAGGER!

◆ During the sixties, Mick Jagger was the most outrageous star on two legs! While The Beatles were charming the hearts of toddlers and grannies alike, everything The Stones did was surrounded by controversy!

The band's hair was considered messy . . . they were never out of court for one thing or another . . . there were mobs everywhere they went.

There really isn't an equivalent to Mick Jagger in the eighties . . . apart from Mick himself!

And it looks like he's *still* wearing the same jersey . . .

SHOCK! HORROR! DISGUST!

LABOUR OF LOVE

Continued from page 49

Diane was Tom's girlfriend, and we got on really well. She was so good to me that I hated to refuse her anything, but I guessed that I wasn't going to like this.

"What does she want?"

Tom looked guilty. "Well, she — er, wondered if you fancied coming out with us tonight."

"What on earth for?" I was starting to get suspicious. Diane and I went out together occasionally, but never with Tom.

Tom had the decency to look uncomfortable. "Well, as a matter of fact, her cousin's come to stay for a while and she thought that maybe . . ."

"What is this?" I interrupted. "Why can no-one leave me alone? Why are you all so determined to find me another boyfriend? I'm OK, you know."

"Is that why you're going around with a box of Kleenex grafted to your hand? Is that why you never go out unless Sue drags you by the hair? Is that why all you talk about is Colin? Because you're OK?"

I stared at him. I hadn't realised I was that bad. I'd thought I was coping pretty well, actually.

"Anyway, she's not matchmaking," Tom said. "She says her cousin's so hideously bad-tempered just now that she couldn't imagine anyone fancying him. She said she wouldn't even ask you but her mum's insisted he comes out with us and she doesn't want him to play gooseberry."

That was OK then. I was sick to death of trying to be polite to guys Sue had fixed me up with, not getting a chance to get to know them, but seeing them immediately as potential Colin replacements, and comparing them to him.

"What time are you going out?"

"In half an hour, so make it snappy."

I did. I didn't see any point in making myself look good when there was no-one I wanted to impress. I just hauled on a pair of jeans and put on some eyeliner — well, I didn't want people fainting in the street at the sight of me without any make-up, did I?

Tom was waiting for me when I came downstairs. Suddenly a thought struck me.

"Where are we going?"

"Just down to the café. Diane and I are going for a drink later."

"The café!" Sue and I never went there these days. "What if Colin comes in with Leah?"

"Show him what a great time you're having without him."

"Oh sure!"

As it turned out, he wasn't there anyway, so I didn't have to worry. I caught sight of Sue playing pool through the back with Diane's sister Claire, and I remembered I'd told her I was staying in. Well, I could explain when she'd finished her game.

Diane waved us over to where she was sitting with a broad, sullen-looking guy with messy blond hair. We sat down, and he glanced up but didn't smile. I was glad. I didn't feel like making an effort to be nice.

"Wendy, this is my cousin Glen — Glen, Wendy."

"Hi."

"Hi."

Silence. "Well," Diane said brightly, "since you two seem to be hitting it off so well, Tom and I will go for a game of pool."

I looked at Glen. Glen looked at me.

"If I hadn't been told," I said carefully, "that this was definitely not another pairing-off stunt, I would be highly suspicious."

"Well, it's not," Glen assured me. "Diane promised. She said you were too bad-tempered to fancy."

I was half-cross and half-amused. "That's what she said about you, too," I told him, before he got too smug.

He scowled. "Anyway, I'm not in the running. I've just split up with someone and I'm still getting over it."

"Me too."

He looked at me with renewed interest. "What happened?"

"The usual. He got bored — fancied someone else."

"Same here. And you should have seen what she went off with! He's a Lofty clone, I swear to God."

I laughed. "Is it our fault if they have no taste?"

"Don't laugh, it's not funny!"

We didn't see head nor tail of Tom or Diane all night, but somehow we didn't really notice. We spent all night arguing, joking, slagging each other off, taking the mick out of each other's problems. Somehow, knowing that we didn't see each other as prospective boyfriend and girlfriend made it much easier for us to get on.

"Blimey!" I said at last. "It's ten o'clock!"

"So it is! I'd better get a move on — I'm going for a drink with Tom and Diane. Coming?"

"I'm only sixteen," I reminded him. "I'll walk home with Sue."

"Will you — er — be here tomorrow night?"

"Well, yes." I smiled. "Yes, I will." I turned round to look for Sue, and I caught her exchanging a thumbs-up sign with Diane. The crafty bitch! She'd engineered it after all.

Glen was watching me. "Do you think we've been taken for mugs here?"

"Could be," I agreed. "But somehow I'm not as angry as I should be."

THE THINGS PEOPLE SAY . . .

Shop assistants, mums, teachers and boyfriends will say almost anything to get you to agree with them/buy something/do something . . . And most of the time they'll be telling complete and utter whoppers!

OUT SHOPPING

"Oh, don't worry about those shoes feeling a bit tight, madam, they'll ease off with wear . . ." What the shoe shop assistant really means is that the tender skin surrounding your toes and the backs of your ankles will ease off, very painfully, as you wear them. If you're in the mood for a bout of torture every time you sport these shoes — go ahead, don't let us put you off!

"It does look a slightly strange colour of green in this light, but when you buy it and take it outside you'll realise that it's exactly the shade you were looking for . . ." Oh, yeah? Only if the colour you were looking for is sea-sick green, that is. Chances are that if the skirt looks that colour in the shop, it'll look that colour in the daylight too. Only take the skirt outside to look at it in the sunlight if the assistant agrees you can do so without buying it — don't part with your money until you have done so.

"It's such a bargain . . ." OK, this is a very persuasive one. We all like to think that we've saved ourselves a fortune, but unfortunately, real bargains are few and far between. Unless you wanted "the bargain" before you left the house, and had been searching the entire town high and low for the last three months, then don't believe this one (even if you're saying it to yourself!). No matter how much money you save, a bargain is only worth it if it's something you were going to buy anyway.

"That really suits you . . ." If the person saying this is your very best friend in the whole world who has no interest whatsoever in winning over your boyfriend or seeing you make a complete fool of yourself, then believe her. If it isn't, don't.

MUM'S THE WORD

"You'll grow into it . . ." This is the classic line that mums always try when you're standing in a school blazer which ends at your knees with sleeves that Cheetah the chimp couldn't fill. Trying to point out that you will not be at school for the next sixty years of your life and that you are already six foot two and not wanting to grow much more anyway will cut no ice whatsoever. Give in and start rolling up those sleeves as soon as possible.

"All the young girls are wearing them . . ." An awkward one, this one. What your mum really means is that all the girls your age *she* admires are wearing them. The fact that you wouldn't be seen dead in anything worn by anyone your mum admires is a complete by the by. Your mother is trying her best to make you hip and trendy and there is absolutely nothing worse.

"It's just a phase . . ." This is a blanket expression which covers all subjects known to man i.e. spots, boyfriend problems, not liking onions, wanting to strangle your little brother . . . The list is absolutely endless and it means absolutely nothing!

"There's a lovely pair of sensible school shoes . . ." Do not make the mistake of immediately bursting into hysterical laughter. Your mother is being serious here and you are on dangerous ground — you may not get a pair of shoes at all if you're not careful. Try the subtle approach instead. Tell her that, unfortunately, your best friend has already bought the exact same shoes and you wouldn't want her to think you were copying her, would you? Your mother will immediately think that your best friend is the greatest thing since sliced bread and that you are being very sensible and mature by not wanting to copy her.

YOUR BOYFRIEND

"Of course I would take you if I thought you would enjoy yourself, but I know you won't so there's no point . . ." What he really means is that he can't think of any better excuse to get out of taking you to his mate's party next Saturday. Tell him that if you're such a stick-in-the-mud bore who can't even entertain herself at a party, you wonder why he goes out with you at all.

"I get the feeling that your mate doesn't like me much . . ." Ohh, beware the boyfriend saying this! Could he be referring to the fact that she caught him out on the town with another girl and emptied her Coke over his head the night before? Or does he just think she might have seen him out on the town . . . Whatever happens, believe one word of his to every five hundred of hers.

"Of course I like you . . . you know that." And there's where he's wrong. If you knew that you wouldn't have had to ask, would you? Point this little known fact out to him and see how he reacts.

"That outfit's a bit on the tarty side, isn't it?" Boyfriends say this only when they're worried that more than one person might catch a glimpse of you, i.e. not just him. You've probably worn the exact same outfit a million times before and he hasn't said a thing, but if he's feeling a touch jealous — watch out! In this type of mood the only outfit he'll like you to go out in is a tarpaulin and ski mask.

"I'll give you a phone when I've sorted myself out . . ." When he's sorted what out? This line simply means that he wants to get out now and nothing anyone says or does is going to make the slightest bit of difference to him. Don't kid yourself he means he'll phone you after he's climbed Everest/led his football team to victory/passed his exams — he's not going to. And why would you want him to . . .? Leave the telephone line clear for someone else to call you!

T·A·K·E·Y·O

Tests have demonstrated that it is possible to ascertain the nature of a subject's emotional make-up and intellectual characteristics by monitoring their responses and reactions to certain visual stimuli. (What? — Ed.) Sorry! What that high-fallutin' lot means is that if you cop a look at the pictures below, and choose one or t'other of the captions we've thrown in, it should be able to tell us something about what kind of person you are. Keep a note of your choices and then you can check yourself out with the list of conclusions.

(a) "Now I know it's true that the good guys always wear white!"
(b) "Are you sure you put the handbrake on?"
(c) "Fancy running out of petrol just like that!"
(d) "It's really peaceful out here. If you kissed me no-one would know."

(a) "If you'd like to sit nearer the front I think I could arrange it!"
(b) "Are you sure the tickets said Wednesday?"
(c) "When you said it was an Invisible Man Convention I thought it would be a meeting of film buffs!"
(d) "Well, they do say that two's company . . ."

(a) "Ever had the feeling that you're spoiled for choice?"
(b) "You two aren't sisters by any chance, are you?"
(c) "Say what you like about my hat, I'm not the one wearing the dog's bowl on my head!"
(d) "How do you fancy a candlelit dinner for two afterwards?"

U R · P I C !

(a) "If she jumps up and down any more I'll faint!"
(b) "Wish I'd brought my sunglasses."
(c) "Trust me to get sprayed from the only puddle on the track."
(d) "Those noisy motorbikes have given me a headache."

(a) "Where on earth did you get those jackets?"
(b) "I don't think my daughter would want to associate with people like you!"
(c) "You mean you're not from the brush company?"
(d) "Hello, it's been ages since I've seen you. Love your hair."

(a) "Right, make any more remarks about my dress and I'll come gunning for you!"
(b) "On your marks, get set . . ."
(c) "Don't you dare pinch my bottom! I'm a Duchess and I'm armed!"
(d) "I hope Andrew's not flying overhead!"

MOSTLY A's

You're a pretty normal sort of person. You tend to mix humour, romance and the obvious in almost everything you do. People find you good fun but a bit flighty at times. Most guys would find you fascinating but you'd need to find someone with the same outlook on life to be really happy. On the party scene you're likely to be the one who'd still like to be dancing at six in the morning and at these times you can often be a pain . . . but a pleasant one!

MOSTLY B's

Do you *ever* have any fun? You spend too much time concentrating on details to enjoy yourself. When you try to tell jokes you usually give away the punch-line before you finish the story and you don't have much of a sense of humour anyway! Your perfect fella would probably be a prospective bank manager or something. Perhaps you should try to let your hair down occasionally and join in the fun . . . it's the only way you're likely to make friends.

MOSTLY C's

For you, life is just one long sit-com. You can't take anything seriously at all. You can always be relied on to keep everyone's spirits up and add a bit of life to the dullest parties. Your ideal man is probably Norman Wisdom . . . you're a sucker for cute guys! No-one can be mad at you for very long and your only problem is stopping giggling long enough to crack the next joke!

MOSTLY D's

You're *such* a romantic! How do you find the time to cram all those niceties and soppy thoughts into your day? You're a big fan of RSC . . . no, not the Royal Shakespeare Company . . . Roses, Sonnets and Chocolates! If Shelley or Keats were still around they'd probably sweep you off your feet with a single glance. Until the man of your dreams shows up you'll just have to keep on dreaming about him.

WRINKLY

WE take a look at some of the

D O N
JOHNSON

C L I N T
EASTWOOD

DONALD WAYNE JOHNSON was born near Galena, Missouri on Dec. 15, 1948. Don was brought up in a log cabin and spent his childhood years on a farm piling hay and tending the animals . . .

He spent his teenage years rarely on the right side of the law and at the age of twelve was locked up in a juvenile detention centre for stealing a car.

As he remembers, *"Most of the guys I hung out with when I was a kid are either dead or in jail now."*

In his late teens, Don won a drama scholarship to The University of Kansas and then joined the ACT — which is roughly the American equivalent of The Royal Shakespeare Company — and moved to San Francisco.

By 1969, Don had moved to Los Angeles and spent most of his time as a hippy, *"staying out all night long, hanging out in coffee shops, talking political trash with every idiot I could find — that was pretty much what I was into."*

Don's first serious relationship began in 1973 when he met Melanie Griffith on a movie set. The couple had a stormy relationship for four years and then got married.

Soon after, they got divorced . . .

His second marriage lasted only a night!
On a night out, he married a girl he'd never met before, woke up with a hangover in the morning and filed for a divorce . . .

Recently, Don split up with Donya Fiorentino, an eighteen-year-old model who soon became the girlfriend of Andrew Ridgeley . . .

As Donia remembers, *"Don was twice my age. He wanted me to stay at home and have babies and do the housework. I was far too young for all of that."*

Don has a five-year-old son named Jesse from his four-year relationship with Patti D'Arbanville . . .

"Kids help to keep you real," he admits. *"I'm more directed now than ever. And living the kind of life that I was always looking for . . ."*

In 1987, Don Johnson launched his musical career and had a Top 40 hit in Britain with "Heartbeat".

While filming "Miami Vice", Don often has to work an eighteen-hour day.
When he first starred in the series, he was being paid 30,000 dollars for each episode. It's rumoured that he makes 100,000 dollars for each episode these days . . .

Don's advice to anyone thinking of becoming an actor is:
"Keep laughing or they'll take you away!"

He was named after his father, Clinton Eastwood, and his mother's name was Ruth. Clint also has a sister called Jean.
"I can't remember my family ever being poor, suffering any hardship as children. Maybe my father did have his worries, but neither Jean nor I ever knew about them."

When he was young, Clint's family moved from town to town quite often, so he doesn't remember being raised in one particular area.

As a kid, Clint was a day-dreamer.
"At school, when I wasn't going crazy trying to catch up on lessons I'd missed, I'd sit there, dreamy-eyed, looking out the window."

After leaving school, Clint struggled along as a lumberjack and then a petrol pump attendant.

Clint was married for twenty-six years until 1979, when he separated from his ex-model wife Maggie and began dating the co-star of many of his movies, Sondra Locke.

He has a nineteen-year-old son, Kyle, and a fourteen-year-old daughter, Alison.

Before taking a part in his first spaghetti-western, Clint appeared in 250 episodes of the American TV series, "Rawhide".

Clint now owns The Hog's Breath Inn — a restaurant near his home where many of the dishes are named after his movies — including the "Fistful Of Dollars Hamburger"!

BUT NICE...
older pin-up people around!

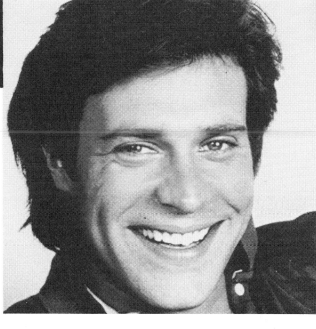

JOHN JAMES

Clint himself doesn't claim to be a great cook. *"I'm certainly not a gourmet chef. I prefer simple dishes like eggs and seafood. I usually only get into the kitchen when I'm left to look after myself."*

He likes to keep fit, too. In the Seventies, he spent one and a half million dollars building himself a gymnasium in his home.

A man of many different roles and faces, Clint confesses, *"I enjoy a movie where I get to wear disguises."*

Films starring Clint Eastwood have taken nearly 500 million dollars at the box-office . . .

Clint believes he's a natural when it comes to acting . . .
"I have a good gut-feeling about the films I make. I don't have a lot of brains and I'm not a well-educated person."

It isn't well-known that Clint Eastwood began his career as a pop singer. He released four singles and an album (which didn't sell very well) before he quit.

He describes his screen image as, *"a super-human character who has all the answers, is doubly cool and exists on his own without society or the help of police forces."*

In April 1986, Clint Eastwood was voted Mayor in his hometown of Carmel, California — so we could be looking at a future President of the USA . . !

JOHN JAMES is really John James Anderson, son of Herb Oscar Anderson, one of New York's most famous radio D.J.'s

John was born in Minnesota on April 18, 1956 and was brought up in Connecticut.

As a youngster he was incapable of stringing two sentences together and so called himself "Captain Klutz". Eventually he found his niche when one of his friends dared him to audition for a part in the school production of "Oklahoma!". He got the part and decided he wanted a career in acting.

He enrolled at Barbara Baxley's Acting School in Westport and then went on to the American Academy of Dramatic Arts in New York. He left the Academy before his graduation to take up a part in the TV soap, "Search For Tomorrow".

He originally auditioned for the part of Steven Carrington in "Dynasty" but the producers didn't think he was suitable for it. However, they were so impressed by his ability that they created the part of Jeff Colby specially for him.

The "Dynasty" producers decided to write another series called the Colbys around the character Jeff. John James was paid £15,000 for each episode, and each episode cost 1.35 million dollars even though it was shot in a studio.

In America, TV bosses decided to axe the show due to low viewing figures. In one of the episodes of the last series, Jeff's wife Fallon was kidnapped by an alien spacecraft!

John met his real-life girlfriend, Marcia Wolf, at a roller-skating party. They literally fell for each other . . . they collided and ended up in a heap on the floor.

He proposed to her, live on television in front of millions of viewers, on the "Tonight" programme in America.

Someone almost broke up his relationship with Marcia by phoning her friends and asking them out on dates . . . telling them that he was John James and imitating his voice perfectly.

He's six foot two inches tall, owns a number of cars and also holds a private pilot's licence. A real high-flyer!

Although he's regarded as a sex-symbol he isn't really a womaniser and had no girlfriends when he was younger. *"I was painfully shy and hopeless at dating because I always said the wrong things. I didn't even go to my graduation dance because I couldn't find a partner!"*

Dear Doctor...

Dr Jennifer Phillips, the Patches very own doctor, answers some of your health queries . . .

● **While undressing the other day, I noticed two large lumps, or spots, on the top and bottom of my nipple. Later they developed whiteheads and a white substance leaked out. I'm really worried about this and I don't want to tell my mother in case she thinks I've got Aids.**
Julie, Dundee.

What you've noticed on your nipples is absolutely normal. It's *not* an indication of Aids or anything else. The swellings you've noticed are actually little glands. It is these glands which produce the "white substance" you noticed.

This white secretion is nature's way of lubricating the nipples when a baby is suckling at the breast. So you see, your breasts are just developing the way they should and there's no need for you to worry.

But don't be tempted to squeeze the "lumps" as this could introduce infection. Leave well alone!

● **My underarms are a very dark colour compared with the rest of my body. I'd be very glad if you could tell me what to do about this.**
Liz, Hastings.

I'm afraid there's very little that can be done about the colour of the skin on your underarms. It's due to an abnormal amount of pigment or melanin under the skin, and there's nothing you can do to remove this.

But don't worry too much about this problem. I'm sure no-one even notices it.

● **I used a new hair remover under my arms recently, and now when I use a deodorant I get a rash which is red and itchy. I've tried just using talc instead, but it doesn't work the same as a deodorant.**
Please tell me what I can do. I'm afraid I might start to smell if I stop using deodorants.
Lynn, E. Sussex.

It's difficult to know whether it was the hair remover or the deodorant which irritated your skin. So give your skin a rest from the hair remover first of all. Shave under your arms when the rash has gone, using a special ladies' shaver. Do this at night and then, in the morning, use your anti-perspirant or deodorant.

And remember — if you start to use a new deodorant or hair remover, always do a patch test first. This will show up any possible allergies or reactions. And also — if you do shave under your arms, *don't* apply deodorant immediately afterwards or they'll have to scrape you off the bathroom ceiling. Always leave a twelve hour gap to let the skin settle down again.

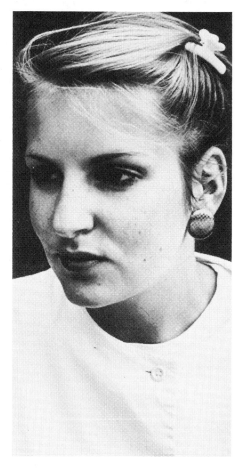

● **I think I'm an abnormal freak. I haven't got any nipples. I've often tried to squeeze them out, but nothing works. I'm worried that when I'm older I won't be able to have sex or babies. Please help.**
Wet Wet Wet Fan, Glasgow.

Please don't distress yourself over this relatively common problem. You're not abnormal — what you have is a condition called inverted nipples. This simply means that your nipples are turned inwards instead of out.

There is no evidence that this causes any trouble and you will certainly be able to enjoy sex and have children. If this hasn't reassured you, though, do visit your own doctor who will put your mind at rest.

● **I think I've got worms and I feel so ashamed. I feel so dirty and I can't understand how I got them because I am a clean person. I'm far too embarrassed to go to the doctor, so could you please tell me the name of something I can ask for at the chemist which will get rid of them?**
Keren, Fife.

There's no need to feel embarrassed or ashamed. Threadworms are more common than you might think. You may have become infected by eating food which had been handled by a child who has threadworms. Children are often not so particular about personal hygiene as you obviously are.

But there is no need to worry — buy an adult pack of Pripsen Granules at the chemist. One dose of this is usually enough to get rid of this annoying condition. As you have realised, it is most important to wash your hands and nails after going to the toilet, especially before eating or handling food.

And by the way, no-one should ever feel embarrassed about going to the doctor for any reason. Doctors have had vast experience in dealing with all sorts of ailments and they'll treat you sympathetically and do their best to put you at ease.

● **I have spots and a very oily skin and I'd like to know if there's anything I can do about it. I keep trying to hide my spots under foundation but because my skin's so greasy, the foundation just goes all shiny and the spots still show.**
Also, my skin's always quite red and that makes me look even worse. What can I do about it? What foundation can I use to hide it and make me look normal?
Beth, Dorset.

I'm sorry you're having so much bother with your complexion. From what you've told me, it rather suggests that you have a condition called Acne Rosacea. Your skin can be greatly helped to return to its natural colour and also become less spotty by taking small doses of Oxytetracycline daily. This is an antibiotic which your doctor can prescribe and I am sure he or she will tell you whether it's necessary in your case.

As far as make-up is concerned, try to use a foundation specially formulated for greasy skin. Also, Boots 17 have brought out a colour corrective powder which you apply over your foundation. A light dusting of this green-tinted powder helps to tone away redness.

Be sparing with it, though, otherwise you'll look like you've got a bad case of sea-sickness!

● I've got a really horrible, embarrassing problem. My feet smell. When I take my shoes off it's like someone just unwrapped a pound of stale cheese. Everyone at school notices it, I'm sure. What can I do about it?

Elaine, Manchester.

Foot odour (or bromidrosis) results from excessive perspiration. There are about 250,000 sweat glands in a pair of feet, pouring out up to half a pint of water a day!

In addition to a thorough daily cleansing routine, using a special foot deodorant will usually get rid of the problem. Also, moisture may be getting trapped inside your shoes. Be sure to change shoes often (letting each pair air out) and wear cotton socks to help absorb the perspiration.

You'll find special foot deodorants in the Scholl range available from Boots and most chemists.

● I'm going to stay for the weekend with my friend and her parents soon but my period's due to start then. I want to know if there's anything you know of which could put my period off for a few days?

I'd feel so embarrassed and ashamed if my period started when I was sleeping at my friend's house, for instance. Please help.

Jean, Coventry.

The only sure way of putting off your period would be for your doctor to prescribe a hormone pill for you. But on the whole, it isn't a good idea to suppress menstruation, especially in young girls who can have erratic periods anyway. You would really have to discuss this with your own doctor and allow him or her to decide whether this was a good idea in your case.

If it isn't, then please don't spoil your weekend worrying about it. Your friend's mother knows all about periods, your friend presumably has periods and they certainly won't make you feel ashamed or embarrassed in any way. And you could always wear panty pads, which are very slim and discreet, just to put your mind at rest.

● I have greasy hair which needs washing four times a week at least, but lately I've noticed to my horror that my hair seems to be falling out much more than it used to. I'm terrified I'm going bald. Should I stop washing my hair so much? My father's forty years old and his hair's starting to thin. Will mine go the same way?

CKTC Fan, Kent.

First of all, although baldness can be hereditary, it's unusual for a father to pass on a tendency to baldness to his daughter. In any case, I'd say that, at forty years old, your father is starting the natural process of ageing, of which thinning hair is a normal part.

Also, people normally lose about 100 hairs per day and, strangely, shedding of hair is heaviest in the winter months and growth is at its peak in the summer. So what you are noticing is probably perfectly normal hair loss.

If you're still worried, though, check with your hairdresser, who'll be able to set your mind at rest and may also recommend a special treatment which might help with your greasy hair problem.

● My hair's so disgusting and so greasy, you could fry chips in it. It gets so bad that my forehead comes out in spots and I'm sure it's because my hair keeps touching it. I brush my hair regularly and always condition it, so why is it so lank and greasy and horrible?

Anne, Newcastle.

Actually, one (or two) reasons could be that you *do* brush your hair regularly and that you *do* condition it. Both these treatments stimulate the hair and scalp, thus encouraging the production of the oils which cause your problem. Try washing your hair every day, using a mild shampoo like Timotei or any brand of baby shampoo. *Don't* put conditioner on afterwards — all that's going to do is add even more oil.

By all means, brush or comb your hair (*not* when it's wet) but don't go mad and brush it 100 times a night — that's only going to stimulate your scalp to produce even more oil.

Finally, if none of these work, do visit your hairdresser. He or she will be able to suggest treatments and styles for your hair to minimise the greasy effect.

● Every time I use washing-up liquid, shampoo, washing powder or whatever, my hands dry up and I come out in a rash. Not only is this rash irritating, it looks awful.

What can I do? I don't want to spend the rest of my life wearing gloves!

Moira, Birmingham.

Basically, you're allergic to detergents. So the only answer is, yes, to wear gloves, but only when you're in contact with detergent. Invest in a pair of rubber gloves and you should have no more rashes.

Or, if you can't face the thought of rubber gloves forever, you could try the Boots' range of sensitive products — washing-up liquid, washing powder, fabric conditioner etc. They're all made specially for sensitive skin and they won't bring you out in a rash. The even better news is that they cost roughly the same as ordinary products!

HOW NOT TO BE SUCCESSFUL

● Treat the house like a hotel/launderette and when your dad grumbles about never being able to get on the phone because of you, suggest sweetly that an extension be installed in your bedroom.

● Always play your Beastie Boys records at full blast — especially when your mum and dad are holding a dinner party for your dad's boss.

● Forget anything to do with birthdays, anniversaries or Christmas — unless it means pressies for you, of course!

● Constructively criticise your mum's cooking, suggesting whole-heartedly that Big Macs for breakfast, lunch and tea would be much more nutritious, convenient and tasty than your mum's attempts at culinary delights.

● It is an excellent idea to ensure that your room is always a pig sty (don't worry about your mum recognising a pig sty, as all parents are experts in pig farming). A healthy selection of dirty socks, old knickers, mouldy burgers

(you got slightly fed-up having them for every meal), talcum powder (ground into your pale pink carpet), and empty Coke cans will impress your mum no end!

● Come in at 3 o'clock in the morning after you promised faithfully you'd be in at 9. If, for some strange reason, your parents ask why you were a teensy bit late — simply say you missed the bus!

● Wear your dad's clothes — he'll appreciate the fact that his daughter admires his taste.

● Throw out all your mum's Roger Whittaker and James Galway albums and explain happily that there just wasn't enough room in the record stand for your Zodiac Mindwarp and Sigue Sigue Sputnik albums.

● 2 days before you're due to go to Bognor on your annual hols with Ma and Pa, explain to them that you can't go because you've already booked 2 weeks in Skegness with Tom/Dick/Harry, whom you met at the disco last Friday. They'll be so proud of your sense of adventure that they'll probably be quite glad to send you packing!

SCHOOL

● Make a point of NEVER EVER arriving at classes on time. When you do finally

get there, rush in chewing gum and spitting, explain that you can't stay because of your dentist/doctor/coffee bar appointment.

● Write your own sick notes and sign them yourself.

● Make sure you sit beside your mate in *all* classes and spend every lesson discussing clothes/boys/discos/Tom/Dick/Harry, and screeching hysterically with laughter. Not only will the rest of the class appreciate a side-show, but the teacher will be impressed with your entertainment value, too.

● However, if your teacher, for some strange and unknown reason, doesn't appreciate your double-act, and splits you and your mate up — scribble notes and throw them across the class to her in the form of paper aeroplanes.

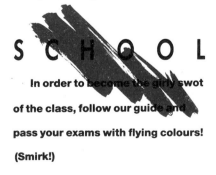

● Only go to school when you're properly dressed — by this we mean cerise pink PVC mini skirt (preferably wet-look), orange fishnet stockings, thigh length boots and black lace vest. To complete the picture, a red mohican would go down a treat!

● Spend every available minute snogging with Tom/Dick/Harry down at the bike sheds which are, incidentally, situated in full view of the staff room.

● NEVER EVER do any homework at all, unless you're threatened with cruelty, and then merely hand in an exact copy of your mate's with illustrations courtesy of the cat/dog/kid brother!

● Offer the headmaster a cigarette, while waiting in the dinner queue.

● Insist upon making a customised denim jacket in the sewing class, while everyone else is making floral circular skirts.

FRIENDS

Wanna be everybody's friend?

Look no further! (Guffaw!)

● When she goes away on her week's holiday, promise faithfully that you'll look after her boyfriend as if he was your own — and do just that!

● After persuading your pal to lend you her brand new slinky white dress (she looks too small/fat/ugly in it anyway), first rip it while running for the bus, then spill Coke or grenadine all over it and return it — telling her the dry cleaner's bill will cost around a tenner.

● When you spot your pal slinking off with THAT biker her mum and dad have threatened to bury, put a note through their door, explaining all — signed 'a well-wisher'.

● Tell her that Wimpy and McDonalds are a low fat diet food.

● Insist on going everywhere her and her new boyfriend go.

● Have it announced over the mike down at the disco, that your friend has just come out of the loo with her skirt tucked up in her knickers!

● Ensure that you tell her that her new boyfriend is too old/young/untrendy, and when you've convinced her, claim him for yourself.

● When your mate has sworn you to secrecy and you've promised that wild horses couldn't drag it from you, make sure that your entire year at school is smirking, pointing and whispering when she goes in on Monday morning.

● When she rushes round to your house, seeking sympathy and comfort because some rat stole her boyfriend while she was on holiday — refuse to see her as you're watching EastEnders/Brookside/The Sky At Night!

● Shriek hysterically with laughter when your friend appears at the disco in her £25 worth of brand new dress. Slag her off for the rest of the evening and make sure she sits in a dark corner so that no-one can see her.

BOYFRIEND

Follow our guide below, and your love life will *never* be the same again (chortle!).

● When his mum invites you round to tea, burp, swing on your chair and leave the meal halfway through, saying you've got something more exciting to do.

● The most important rule here is to criticise his friends at every available opportunity, pointing out how immature/stupid/pathetic they are. Don't just mention it once or twice — go on all night until he gets the point.

● Discover who his worst enemy is and, the next time you go to the disco together, make a bee-line for him.

● Completely ignore him when he's out with his friends.

● Whisper and giggle hysterically with your mate, whenever he passes you in the corridor.

● Always say 'you'd be really nice if . . . you looked like Tom Cruise/Rob Lowe/Tom/Dick/Harry'.

● Rant on and on about make-up, clothes, Jon Bon Jovi, Tom/Dick/Harry and then stomp off in a huff when he mentions football.

● Ignore all hints about his approaching birthday and when it does arrive, offer to treat him to an expensive meal. After you've eaten it, refuse to pay!

● Wait for a night when it's pelting with rain, and then stand him up.

● Take your mate along when he's planned a romantic meal for two at the local Italian restaurant.

BRUCE WILLIS

TIMOTHY DALTON

WALTER BRUCE WILLIS was born on March 19, 1955 in Germany, where his father was stationed in the army. His family moved back to America soon after, so Bruce spent most of his childhood and teenage years in New Jersey.

After leaving school, Bruce spent a while in some pretty boring jobs, as well as playing harmonica in a local group.

Soon after, Bruce was accepted on an acting course at Montclair State School. According to reports, he didn't spend much time in classes . . . !

It was around 1977 when Bruce bought a one-way ticket to New York and, after a few auditions, landed himself a part in a movie called "Fool For Love".

After that, he played a reporter in a film called "The Verdict", as well as making a couple of small appearances in "Prince Of The City" and "The First Deadly Sin".

Around 1984 in Los Angeles, Bruce heard that there were auditions being held for the part of Madonna's punky boyfriend in "Desperately Seeking Susan".

He turned up dressed in torn T-shirt and jeans with tattoos, earrings and his head shaved!

He didn't get the part . . .

Even so, it worked out to his advantage. At the same time, Bruce got wind (har!) . . . of the fact that there were other auditions being held by ABC television for a new comedy series.

Still dressed in his punky gear, he arrived with a

"Hi! I'm Bruce Willis. Let's do it!" — and got the part of David Addison in "Moonlighting" . . .

The first time his co-star Cybill Shepherd caught sight of him, she thought he was really cute . . .

"The first time Bruce and I met, sparks flew. He is very attractive and very, very funny.
"Mind you, sometimes he really gets on my nerves. On the set, he never stops laughing, singing, cracking jokes . . ."

Of his character in "Moonlighting", Bruce says, *"David's got this shield, this armour, which is his humour. But he really is a big kid who's never been forced to accept the responsibility of adulthood."*

Bruce's father wasn't too keen on him pursuing a career in acting and would have much preferred him to follow in his own footsteps and become a welder . . .

On being a sex-symbol . . .

"I'm always confused when people say that. I don't really understand what they mean. I've never looked on myself as a sex symbol. It seems like they're talking about someone else."

Bruce is worth a lot of money these days . . .
He picks up £850,000 a year for "Moonlighting". He also received a cool £2 million for his recording contract with Motown and expects to make around £15 million in the next three years . . .

He's always been confident about his talent . . .
"I never doubted the fact that even if it took five years or ten years or fifteen years, it was going to happen. So when it did, I just thought "Good, there it is."

TIMOTHY DALTON was born in Colwyn Bay, North Wales on March 21, 1946. His father was an advertising executive and his grandparents were music hall performers.

He saw his first James Bond film when he was fifteen, but surprisingly, it didn't inspire him to act.

He decided he wanted to become an actor when he was sixteen after seeing a production of Shakespeare's "Macbeth".

Timothy was chosen from an impressive list of "would-be" James Bonds . . .
Among those considered were Mel Gibson, Oliver Tobias, Lewis Collins, Ian Ogilvy and James Brolin.

He was asked once before to play James Bond — at the age of 25. Eventually he turned the offer down because he felt he was too young.

Timothy thinks the ideal James Bond should be between the ages of 35 and 40 and confesses that he thinks Sean Connery played the role far better than he does.

Timothy played Prince Barin in "Flash Gordon" and Heathcliff in "Wuthering Heights".

To relax, he enjoys fishing . . .
"I've been obsessed with fishing ever since I was three years old and went with my grandfather on my first expedition to the local pier."

DAVID
BOWIE

"The only tackle I had was a ball of string and a bent pin, but I've never forgotten what a glorious experience it was!"

He had a relationship with Vanessa Redgrave for a few years and has been romantically linked with Stephanie Powers recently . . .

While working on a film called "Sextette", Timothy acted alongside screen legend Mae West — who was 85 at the time!
"She lived up to her reputation as a flirt! She tried flirting with me and it was an experience I wouldn't have missed for anything.
"For as long as I live, I'll never forget the twinkle in her eyes as she sized me up!"

Timothy studied the character of James Bond before making his first film, and recognises a difference between the Bond on screen and the Bond in the books.

"In the books you're dealing with a real man, not a superman. He's often uncertain and sometimes gets very frightened and nervous. That doesn't come across in the films."

Unlike James Bond, Timothy doesn't particularly like flashy cars, but admits that like his screen character, he does have a passion for scrambled eggs!

He was recently offered £200,000 to advertise American Express as James Bond — but turned it down!

On his acting career, Timothy comments . . .
"I have tried to be different over the years. I didn't want to be too closely identified with just one thing."

DAVID ROBERT JONES, alias David Bowie, was born on the 8th of January 1947. He was brought up in Bromley where he went to Bromley Technical High School. While he was there he joined the cubs and the school choir and also learned to play the clarinet and tenor saxophone.

His first appearance on stage with a band was when he formed a band called George and the Dragons for a school concert. He got into a fight over a girl — injuring his eye — and later needed delicate surgery. His eyes are now different colours.

He became interested in Buddhism and actually spent some time in a Buddhist monastery. At one point he was only a month away from becoming a monk!

In 1970, after the success of "Space Oddity", he said he didn't know how long he'd stay in pop music. *"I never plan ahead and I'm very fickle and always change my mind about things. I never expected Space Oddity to be the success it was and it's all rather overwhelmed me. I couldn't tell you what I'll be doing this time next year, but I'm quite happy at the moment."*

His acting career has been as impressive as his music career and he has starred as John Merrick in the Broadway production of "The Elephant Man" as well as films such as, "The Man Who Fell To Earth", "The Hunger", "Merry Christmas Mr Lawrence", "Absolute Beginners", "Labyrinth", and "Into The Night"! Wottabusyboy!

In the past few years he's done a lot of work to help charity. He was one of the main people behind Live Aid and gave up part of his time on stage at Wembley to show a moving film of starving children made by a Canadian film crew and backed by the Cars' song, "Drive". David teamed up with Mick Jagger before Live Aid to make their own video of "Dancing in the Street". They had originally intended to do it live by satellite link-up but there was a couple of seconds delay on the signal which made it impossible. All the money from the video and the single went to Band Aid.

In 1983 he held a benefit concert to raise cash for the Brixton Neighbourhood Community Association. Tickets were priced at £25 and £50 each!

The idea for his video of the single "Absolute Beginners" was stolen from a cult TV commercial of the '60's . . . for cigarettes. People were supposed to identify with the lonely character on London's Westminster Bridge and the message, "You're never alone with a Strand". And they were all supposed to rush out in their thousands and buy Strand cigarettes. Only nobody did and the TV commercial went down in history as the biggest floperooni of all time.

He sent his son Zowie to the same school as Prince Charles, Prince Andrew and Prince Edward . . . Gordonstoun in Aberdeenshire.

David boxes fifteen rounds every day with a sparring partner and is also a championship standard skier.

Amid rumours that he's quitting music he says, *"I'm spending more time on films, and have a couple of exciting projects lined up, but that doesn't mean I'm finished with music."* Remember what he said in 1970 anyone?

GIRLS

They say: "I can't come out with you tonight. I've got to wash my hair, clean my room and cat-sit for my granny's kitten."
They mean: "You have a face like a mouldy pizza, all the depth and charisma of a Rice Krispie and I wouldn't go out with you for a million pounds."

They say: "Your hair looks great. I wish I had hair as curly as yours."
They mean: "You swine! Why do boys always have lurverly girly hair . . . I hate you, I hate you!"

They say: "You've got to help me! The teacher'll never believe that my homework was mangled under a bus wheel when I rescued an old lady from certain death."
They mean: "Please, please, please can I copy your homework 'cos I haven't done mine and, if you don't let me copy it, I won't let you take me to the pictures tomorrow night, so there!"

They say: "I'd love to wear something really stunning when we go out on Saturday, just so long as it isn't too short or too revealing."
They mean: "I'd love to be outrageous but I'm a coward and I've got the figure of a bull elephant, so I'll just wear a frumpy frock and a baggy old sweater."

They say: "Of course I won't tell your mates how romantic you are."
They mean: "What was your best friend's phone number?"

They say: "No!"
They mean: "No!"

They say: "What a lovely present! I've always wanted a turquoise and brown pullover."
They mean: "My God! That's the most disgusting item of clothing I've ever laid eyes on! Are you colour blind?"

They say: "Your mate Gary's a creep. I don't know what all those stupid girls see in him."
They mean: "I just tried to chat Gary up and he told me he didn't pinch his mates' girlfriends."

BOYS

They say: "I can't see you tonight. I've got football practice."
They mean: "Me and my mates are going to play pool at the youth club and chat up these new girls from school."

They say: "You look gorgeous tonight."
They mean: "Normally I think you look like a dog's dinner but tonight you've got some money and I'm skint."

They say: "I really can't understand why that guy spends all his time going out with so many different girls . . . I'm much happier to be going steady with you."
They mean: "What's that skinny creep got that I don't? He gets all the good-looking girls and I'm stuck with you!"

They say: "No-one understands me."
They mean: "I'm a rampaging psychopath."

They say: "You weren't really scared by that film on T.V. last night, were you?"
They mean: "My little sister had to tell me all about it this morning 'cos I spent the whole time hiding behind the settee."

DO THEY *REALLY* MEAN THAT?

Sometimes (gasp shock horror) boys (and girls) say things they don't really mean. So to help you sort out the sweet-talking nonsense from the genuine article, here's our Patches guide to what boys (and girls) say — and what they really mean . . .

They say: "When I'm older I'm going to be incredibly wealthy!"
They mean: "I don't fancy the idea of having to work for a living so I'm hoping someone will leave me their fortune when they pass away."

They say: "I'm not all that keen on sport."
They mean: "I'm such a complete incompetent I can't even kick a football without falling flat on my face . . . but I can knit a cardigan in no time at all!"

They say: "I'd rather you didn't tell anyone we're going out together . . . not for a while at least."
They mean: "I've got another girlfriend."

They say: "(Any soppy poetry he may like to recite to you)."
They mean: "I'm such a boring wimp I can't think of anything at all to say so I may as well babble nonsense."

They say: "I bought you this rose because it reminded me of you."
They mean: "I couldn't find any place selling artichokes!"

Making Your Mind Up

E

SISTERS! I DON'T UNDERSTAND THEM! LAST WEEK, SHE TOLD ME SHE STILL LIKED PETE, BUT NOW SHE SAYS SHE DOESN'T. OH, WELL . . .

At school —

IT'S ONLY A SLOW PUNCTURE. IF I PUMP IT UP I CAN RIDE HOME.

But . . .

YOU STUPID BRAT! YOU'RE NOT SUPPOSED TO RIDE ON THE PAVEMENT!

I'D BETTER NOT STOP. HE SOUNDS A BIT ANNOYED.

I went back home and put the bike in the shed. Then . . .

HI, DON.

OH, HECK! IT'S HIM — THE ONE I KNOCKED OVER! HE MUST BE JANET'S NEW BOYFRIEND!

I decided the best thing would be to hide . . .

MUM'S NOT HOME YET. I'D BETTER NOT GO OUT UNTIL SHE GETS BACK. SHE DOESN'T LIKE BILLY BEING LEFT ALONE. HE'S LIABLE TO WRECK SOMETHING — LIKE THE HOUSE.

WHO'S BILLY?

MY LITTLE BROTHER. HE'S A TOTAL HORROR.

CAN THIS BE ME SHE'S TALKING ABOUT?

NEVER MIND YOUR BROTHER. LET'S MAKE THE MOST OF OUR TIME SEEING AS WE'RE ALL ALONE.

DON . . . NO . . .

Then suddenly I got some dust up my nose and . . .

AAAATISHOO!!

And . . .

THAT'S THE KID WHO KNOCKED ME OVER!

BILLY! WHAT ARE YOU DOING THERE?

WELL, EVERYBODY'S GOT TO BE SOMEWHERE.

'COURSE THEN THEY BOTH GOT ANNOYED WITH ME, THEN MUM CAME HOME AND JOINED IN AND I GOT SENT TO BED EARLY. HUH! LUCKY I HAD A SECRET STORE OF BISCUITS UNDER MY PILLOW OR I MIGHT HAVE STARVED TO DEATH.

Next day . . .

I'VE GOT TO MEND A PUNCTURE ON JANET'S BIKE, PETE, BUT I CAN'T FIND THE TOOL KIT. CAN I BORROW YOURS?

WELL, I'M NOT DRESSED YET. TELL YOU WHAT, I'LL BRING IT ROUND AS SOON AS I CAN.

I WISH YOU WERE STILL GOING OUT WITH JANET. HER NEW BOYFRIEND'S REALLY HORRIBLE.

I WISH I WAS TOO, BILLY. I STILL LIKE HER A LOT.

NO HOPE, PETE. SHE TOLD ME SHE DIDN'T WANT TO SEE YOU AGAIN. SHAME. HER BOYFRIENDS ARE ALL BORING, BUT YOU WERE QUITE NICE.

COMING FROM YOU, BILLY, THAT HAS TO BE A COMPLIMENT.

When I got back home, Janet was all done up, even though it was only 8.30 in the morning . . .

YOU SHOULDN'T HAVE GONE ROUND TO PETE'S SO EARLY. I BET HE WASN'T EVEN UP.

WELL, IT WAS YOUR IDEA FOR ME TO BORROW HIS TOOLS.

HE ASKED ABOUT YOU BUT I TOLD HIM YOU DIDN'T LIKE HIM ANYMORE.

OH, DID YOU? I THOUGHT I TOLD YOU TO MIND YOUR OWN BUSINESS. I HAPPEN TO LIKE PETE A LOT.

WHY CAN'T YOU MAKE UP YOUR MIND? I THOUGHT YOU WERE GOING OUT WITH THAT DON?

DON WAS A DEAD LOSS. HE WAS A SLIME-BALL. I'M NOT SEEING HIM AGAIN. BUT THAT DOESN'T MEAN I WANT PETE BACK . . . NOT NECESSARILY . . .

Pete soon appeared with his tool kit . . .

HERE'S THE TOOLS, BILLY. I'LL GIVE YOU A HAND TO FIX THAT PUNCTURE.

OK, BUT YOU'RE NOT GETTING ANY OF THE MONEY JANET'S PAYING ME.

OH, HI, PETE! FANCY COMING IN FOR A COFFEE?

THANKS. THAT SOUNDS LIKE A GREAT IDEA, JANET.

HOI! YOU'RE SUPPOSED TO BE HELPING ME.

They were gone an awful long time, so I went to investigate . . .

HUH! THAT'S NOT DRINKING COFFEE!

I DIDN'T THINK I'D MISS YOU SO MUCH, PETE. I TRIED TO PRETEND I DIDN'T LIKE YOU BUT IT WASN'T TRUE. I'M GLAD YOU FEEL THE SAME WAY.

All that soppy stuff must have had an effect on Janet. She started being nice to me!

YOU DID SOMETHING RIGHT FOR ONCE. I'VE MADE IT UP WITH PETE. THANKS, BILLY.

BUT I DIDN'T DO ANYTHING.

OH, YES YOU DID. IF YOU HADN'T GONE TO SEE HIM HE WOULDN'T HAVE COME ROUND WITH THE TOOLS FOR THE BIKE, AND I WOULDN'T HAVE HAD A CHANCE TO MAKE THINGS UP WITH HIM.

BUT I ONLY DID THAT 'COS I COULDN'T FIND MY TOOL KIT.

OF COURSE YOU COULDN'T. I HID IT. THAT WAS WHY I SUGGESTED YOU CALL ON PETE. I GUESSED HE WOULDN'T BE UP.

AND YESTERDAY SHE SHOUTED AT ME FOR TELLING PETE SHE STILL FANCIED HIM! I'LL NEVER UNDERSTAND SISTERS!

THE END

There's more to mohair than woolly pullys.

Maybe she doesn't want to be recognised.

FUTURE SHOCK

Ever felt that the last thing fashion designers have in their minds when they make clothes is that people actually have to wear them? Well, this group of students have taken things into their own hands and created a mixture of truly wild and wacky outfits. Your mother might not like it but they're a lot more fun than a pair of banana leggings and a fuchsia sweater. This little lot are from the Edinburgh College of Art Fashion and Theatre Costume Show.

A stage outfit you'd be sure to cut the ice in.

Inspired by strawberries on the lawn?

You'd never be mistaken for a wallflower in this.

Looks like he shelled out so much for the suit, there wasn't any dosh left for shoes.

Cinderella à la Westwood.

69

IT'S A DOG'S LIFE

As far as animal charities go, most people have only heard of the RSPCA and the PDSA — and maybe the Dogs' Home Battersea. But there are lots more than that — Patches takes a look at one or two . . .

Want a laugh? The British are supposed to be a nation of animal lovers! Good one, isn't it?

You might be excused for thinking that it's perfectly true — but the existence of so many animal charities proves that there's a lot more cruelty about than you might like to believe. You might remember the story about the three puppies who were Sellotaped together in a suitcase and left to die. Fortunately they were found in time, but there must be lots of others who aren't so lucky.

But the animal charities are here to try to stop this sort of thing from happening, and to rescue strays and badly treated animals from cruelty, whether it's deliberate or just happening through ignorance.

THE NATIONAL CANINE DEFENCE LEAGUE

The NCDL has 13 centres throughout Britain for lost, unwanted and abandoned dogs. NO HEALTHY DOG IS EVER DESTROYED. They provide vaccination for every dog brought into their care, and try to find homes for all of them. There is also a "Dog Sponsor" scheme, where dog lovers can adopt the long term residents of the kennels. Some of the dogs can be in the kennels for quite a long time — like Jason.

Quite a few years ago, a scruffy brown and white dog was taken into one of the NCDL centres from a police station. The staff called him Jason, and he soon settled down into kennel life although he didn't like any other dog approaching him. The visitors who came round all liked him, and before long he was offered a new home. At first he seemed to be settling in well, but then he took it into his head to come back to the kennels. It took him quite a while to get back, but finally he made it.

Over the next few years, Jason went to several homes, but he always returned to the kennels. All the staff thought he was a bit special, and if he did get a little fat from all the tit-bits he was given then no-one seemed to mind.

As the years passed, Jason mellowed and he no longer tried to fight all the other dogs. He was often seen looking after his kennel mate like an old grandfather, and he never seemed to mind that they all went to new homes and he was left behind. Towards the end of 1986 he began to get quieter — old age was catching up with him. No-one knew for sure how old he was, but he'd been at the kennels for at least ten years.

On Christmas Eve all the staff went round giving tit-bits to their charges. Everyone was happy and the dogs seemed to know that it was a special time of the year. At feed time, Jason was given his dinner out in his run as usual, so that his friend didn't eat it all. When the kennel assistant went round ten minutes later, she saw Jason lying beside his dish. She carried him to the office, but he was found to be dead — the vet confirmed that a heart attack had killed him instantly.

If Jason had lived in a home he could not have been missed more. The staff felt that they hadn't only lost a friend, but a very special character who in the end had done as he had often done before — quickly and quietly slipped away.

70

SOME OF THE DOGS FROM NCDL CENTRES . . .

SAM was found chained up and very thin. He is blind in one eye because of a blow, and completely deaf, again because of ill treatment. Now he's nine years old, and very happy and fat!

DYLAN was brought in because his owners kept going abroad. He's been rehomed three times but he keeps coming back!

DARCY was very thin when he was brought in by police. He's now very lovable and affectionate, but he's never been offered a new home.

MINDY was kicked repeatedly before being brought to NCDL. He's a labrador cross greyhound, and he likes females but not males.

THE HORSE RESCUE FUND

The Horse Rescue Fund is based in Suffolk, and one of their main concerns is trying to improve conditions at sales. The BBC documentary "We Shoot Horses Don't We" featured some of the work of the fund, and though it's not as well known as HAPPA or the Bransby Home of Rest, it does every bit as good a job.

Other areas of concern are the shooting of horses from helicopters in Australia, and shipments of horses to Uruguay. If you write to the address given below, the fund will send you details of their work and how you can help.

TREACLE is a black colt who was rescued at a sale. He was in very poor condition, with split and infected hooves. Now Treacle has made a great recovery and he's very playful!

Treacle before

Treacle after

RSPCA/SSPCA

Probably the best-known of all the animal charities, the Royal and Scottish Societies For Prevention of Cruelty to Animals deal with wild animals, farm and domestic, and research animals. These Societies have more to do with the legal side of things, and quite often can't take any action against the owners of the badly treated animals until it's too late for the animal in question.

New inspectors are put through seven months of rigorous training. Subjects they must study include animal handling, police law and court procedures. Theoretical work is backed up by three months practical training alternating between rural and urban stations.

There are lots of other animal charities which we didn't have the space to mention, but we've listed a few addresses below of organisations that you might like to support. Many have sponsor schemes where you can sponsor one of the residents at the kennels or stables and help with their upkeep. Remember to enclose an SAE when you write.

ADDRESSES

THE NATIONAL CANINE DEFENCE LEAGUE,
1 Pratt Mews,
London NW1 0AD.

THE HORSE RESCUE FUND,
The Walbancke Family,
English Cottage,
Great Common,
Ilketshall St. Andrew,
N. Beccles, Suffolk.

THE CATS PROTECTION LEAGUE,
17 Kings Road,
Horsham,
West Sussex, RH13 5PP.

INTERNATIONAL LEAGUE FOR THE PROTECTION OF HORSES,
67a Camden High Street,
London NW1 7JL.

WORLD WILDLIFE FUND,
Panda House,
11-13 Ockford Road,
Godalming,
Surrey, GU7 1QU.

ROYAL SOCIETY FOR PREVENTION OF CRUELTY TO ANIMALS,
The Causeway,
Horsham, Sussex, RH12 1HG.

BEAUTY FOR

No matter what time of year it is, you can still look your best

WINTER

Time for a new beginning. This is the best time of year for cleaning out your wardrobe and make-up bag and starting again from scratch. So make a few resolutions — and stick to them!

CLEAN UP!

Winter is the hardest time of year for your skin. The cold weather and strong winds can dry out your skin very quickly, and even oily skin can become red and scaly.

The most important thing for all skin types is moisturiser. Always apply your moisturiser just after cleansing so you can trap the small amount of dampness left next to your skin.

If you have dry skin, a cream is best (try Crookes Cream E45 or Ponds Cold Cream) while greasy skin can make do with a light lotion or milk (Simple or Ponds Cocoa Butter).

Once a week, it's a good idea to use a face pack or mask to remove the dead skin cells. Be sure you choose one to suit your skin type, though, as some of them are too strong for very dry or delicate skin.

Remove every last scrap of make-up at night by using a cleanser and cotton wool. If you don't feel really clean without a wash, use cleanser first (cream for dry skin, lotion for greasy) and then wash with a mild soap like Simple or Pears.

Rinse it off well, then use a toner to remove every last drop of cleanser and soap, as any left behind will irritate your skin and act like a magnet to dirt.

As well as your regular morning and evening cleansing routine, remember to apply more moisturiser before you go outside so that your skin is protected from the weather.

BODY BEAUTIFUL

The skin on your body is going to suffer by being trapped under all those winter woollies most of the day.

As there's no room for air to circulate, any sweat will be trapped next to your skin and could cause greasiness and spots or blackheads on your back and shoulders.

Remedy this by using a back brush or loofah in the bath to get your circulation going and, after you've dried yourself, ask your mum to put some spot lotion or astringent over your back and shoulders.

HANDY HINTS

Unless you wear gloves every time you step out of the door, you'll probably find your

hands starting to get a bit red and dry.

Try to keep them out of water as much as possible (wear rubber gloves when you're washing clothes, dishes or even cleaning out the goldfish bowl!).

Moisturise your hands after washing and, if things get really bad, cover them with Vaseline, slip on a pair of cotton gloves (available from Boots or chemists) and leave for a few hours or overnight. When you take them off, your hands should be much softer.

LIPS

Your lips also suffer a lot in winter because of the cold and wind.

Use a lipsalve like Chapstick or Lypsyl every time you go outside and before going to bed. Nothing looks worse than chapped, flaking lips and they're very easily prevented.

HOT HAIR TIPS

● Keep your hair covered in really cold weather. In freezing temperatures, hair can become really dry and brittle and might even split. If you don't like wearing hats, wrap a bright scarf around your head.

● If keeping your hair covered means it gets greasy faster, be sure to use a mild shampoo every time you wash it and don't have the water too hot. Strong shampoos and hot water both encourage greasiness.

● Use conditioner after every wash.

● If you find your hair looking a bit dry and dull, try a hot oil treatment or a temporary colour to brighten it up.

GET MOVING!

Whatever you do, don't use all those baggy clothes as an excuse for stuffing yourself silly on puddings!

You'll only be sorry when

Spring comes around and you shed your jumpers to discover you bear more than a passing resemblance to a pudding yourself!

Because of the bad weather, you're probably not going out as much as usual but, the bad news is, there are lots of sports you can take part in indoors.

Badminton, for instance, uses about 80 calories every ten minutes and dancing, up to 120 calories in ten minutes.

One of the best winter exercises is swimming — nearly everyone has a heated pool in their town and, as well as toning up almost every muscle in you body, you'll use about 100 calories in ten minutes.

f you follow our Patches seasonal guide to looking good

SPRING

At last, the first glimmer of sunshine — and it's time to start planning summer holidays and dieting for that bikini!

TONE UP

If you've been eating healthily all winter you shouldn't have put on much weight (if any), and all you should have to do is a daily exercise routine to tone up your muscles.

If you're going to exercise, remember that you'll need to do it regularly and the results may take a few weeks to show.

Before you start, take some time to warm up by slow running on the spot, toe-touching and some gentle stretching exercises. Then you can start to exercise properly.

We don't have room here to show you lots of exercise routines but here are a few for problem areas.

Double Chin

Stick out your chin and push your lower teeth out and over the upper ones. Then nod your head up and down as you turn it slowly from left to right. And, even if it doesn't work, you'll have given your little brother a good laugh!

Stomach

Sit with your back to a wall. With your feet slightly apart, point your toes, then stretch your legs straight out and criss-cross them like scissors as you lift them a few inches off the floor, then gently lower them down again, criss-crossing all the time.

Stomach, Thighs and Bottom

Kneel on the floor and hold your arms straight out in front of you. Now rock back and forth very slowly, as far as you can in each direction. Repeat for as long as you can.

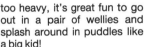
WATERBABY

This is the season of April showers and, if the rain's not too heavy, it's great fun to go out in a pair of wellies and splash around in puddles like a big kid!

Fresh rainwater is great to wash your hair and face in. It will leave your skin and hair feeling really soft — but only if you live in a small town or out in the country. A splash of grime-laden rainwater collected in the middle of London isn't going to do your complexion much good!

STYLE SETTING

Now's the ideal time to start thinking about a new hairstyle for summer.

Choose something short and easy to keep or, if you're determind to have long hair, try a perm.

Perms are ideal for holiday time as all you have to do is wash them and leave them. At night, a blob of gel is all you need to use before hitting the Benidorm nightspots with Manuel.

Don't try a home perm but go along to your hairdresser and ask his advice first. After all, he knows best and will be able to choose the ideal perm for your hair type.

DO-IT-YOURSELF BEAUTY

Wake up your skin and really get it glowing with some of our homemade beauty treatments.

For Oily Skin

Wash a large, ripe tomato and, after removing the skin, mash well with a fork. Spread over your face, leave for 20 minutes, then rinse off.

For Dry Skin

Mash a banana in a bowl along with one tablespoon of clear honey. Spread over your face and leave for 20 minutes before rinsing off.

For Blackheads and Oily Skin

Put 2 peeled, cored apples into an electric blender with one tablespoon of lemon juice. Leave this mask on your face for just ten minutes.

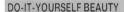

SUMMER

Time for holidays and lots of relaxation. Summer is the time of year most of us look our best, so make the most of it!

GOLDEN BROWN

Nearly everyone likes to have a tan in summer and although a little sunshine is good for you, don't overdo it.

Tanning Tips

● Always, always use a sun tan lotion. This will protect you from too much sun all at once and stop you ending up looking like a lobster.

● Remember that ultraviolet rays (the ones which tan) travel through water, so don't go swimming without wearing a suntan lotion and re-apply it after you've finished your swim.

● Don't wear make-up or perfume while sunbathing. The chemicals in them could react with the sunlight and leave you covered in blotches or badly burned.

● Use a total sunblock on sensitive areas like lips and eyelids or you could have a very painful holiday!

● Don't sunbathe between eleven o'clock and two o'clock. That's when the sun's rays are at their strongest and most harmful.

HAIR CARE

Sunshine can be pretty hard on your hair, especially if it's blonde, permed or coloured.

It's best not to have your hair permed or coloured just before going on holiday. Have a perm at least two weeks beforehand and leave colouring until you come back.

Any shade of dye can react with sunlight causing weird colour changes or dryness and frizziness.

If you decide to go ahead with perms or colour anyway, cover your hair when sunbathing or smother it with conditioner before going out. When you wash it off, your hair will be soft and silky.

GET FRESH!

Instead of stuffing yourself with ice-cream and fattening paella or pasta, choose fresh fruit and vegetables to eat on holiday. It will be cheap, tasty and, best of all, has hardly any calories.

You'll also notice your hair, skin and eyes improving in appearance because of all the extra vitamins.

EYE, EYE

Our eyes are two of the most delicate organs in our bodies, so it makes sense to look after them as well as you can.

Wear sunglasses as much as possible during the summer and, when you go to buy a pair, make sure they're going to do their job properly.

The lenses of sunglasses have to be really dark to work properly. Try them on and look at yourself in a mirror. If you can still see your own eyes, the lenses are too light.

Generally speaking, glass lenses are better than plastic as they won't warp and are less easily damaged.

FEET FIRST

Summer is the only time of year your feet will be on display, so now's the time to pay more attention to them.

Give your feet a treat with a refreshing pedicure.

You'll need:
A big bowl of soapy water
A pumice stone
Toenail clippers or scissors
Cuticle cream
An orange stick
Body lotion.

First of all, soak your feet in a basin for at least five minutes. Dry them, paying special attention to the area between your toes.

Now use the pumice stone to remove any dead, hard skin and rinse and dry your feet again.

Clip your toenails straight across and use the cuticle cream and orange stick to gently ease the cuticles back.

Now rub in lots of moisturiser or body lotion and leave your shoes and socks off for as long as possible.

AUTUMN

Now that summer's over, it's time to start preparing yourself for winter and trying to keep that summer glow for as long as possible.

OUT AND ABOUT

Now that the weather's getting colder, it's easy to spend lots of time in front of the T.V., eating and drinking.

Well, don't. You'll only get fat and lazy and your skin and hair will suffer from spending so much time indoors.

Walking is one of the best exercises for autumn. The scenery is lovely at this time of year, so there's plenty to look at, and, as long as you wear warm clothes, you'll be quite comfortable.

If walking doesn't appeal to you, check the local press for details of night classes near you.

Enrolment is always at this time of year and there are loads of classes to choose from: badminton, dance and keep-fit are always really popular.

If you don't fancy anything that energetic, try yoga — it's very relaxing and great fun.

COLOUR UP

No matter how careful you were with your hair this summer, it's probably looking a bit dry and dull just now.

Brighten it up with lots of moisture treatments and then try one of the autumn hair shades.

Wash-in, wash-out hair colourants are cheap, easy-to-use and won't harm the condition of your hair.

Of course, they'll only last until you wash your hair and you might want a more permanent change.

If you do, it's best to go to your hairdresser. He or she will know your hair well and will be able to tell which shades will work best on your hair and how they'll affect the condition of it.

BATHING BEAUTY

After summer, your skin is probably a bit dry and dull, too, so you have to try to put some of the moisture back.

Before you have a bath, massage yourself with body lotion and wait for at least five minutes before getting into the bath.

Then soak for at least ten minutes in a warm (not hot) bath with a few drops of olive oil added.

Next, use a body brush or loofah to get rid of all those dead skin cells and let what's left of your tan shine through.

Pat yourself dry with a soft towel and then moisturise again.

KEEPING COOL

Now that the cooler weather is back, the winter woollies have probably been dragged out of the wardrobe again and it's sweaty armpit time.

Yes we know, it's not a very pleasant subject but, after all, it doesn't matter how you look, if you don't feel dry and fresh, you won't feel good.

There are two types of product available to you — deodorant and anti perspirant.

Deodorant doesn't stop you sweating. As the name suggests it's basically just a perfume to cover up the smell of sweat.

Anti-perspirant contains a chemical which actually blocks the sweat ducts and although it won't stop you sweating completely, it will reduce the sweating a lot.

Most anti-perspirants contain a deodorant too.

Most of these products come in roll-on, spray-on and solid form and all of these have their advantages and disadvantages.

Roll-ons are usually the cheapest but take a few minutes to dry, while aerosols dry straight away but aren't quite as effective. Solids also dry immediately and are very effective but tend to leave white marks on your clothes.

The LAST

Even the plainest outfit can be brought to life with the right accessories.
understated, try just

Go for

DETAIL...

If you're out to attract attention, go for excess, or if you want to be more
one simple brooch.

Bold

Stockists: Earrings, bracelets etc.
from Joe Cool and Flash Trash.
Car badge from Joe Cool.
Socks and gloves from C & A.
Wallet and stationery from Top
    Shop.
    Bag and scarf from Top Shop.

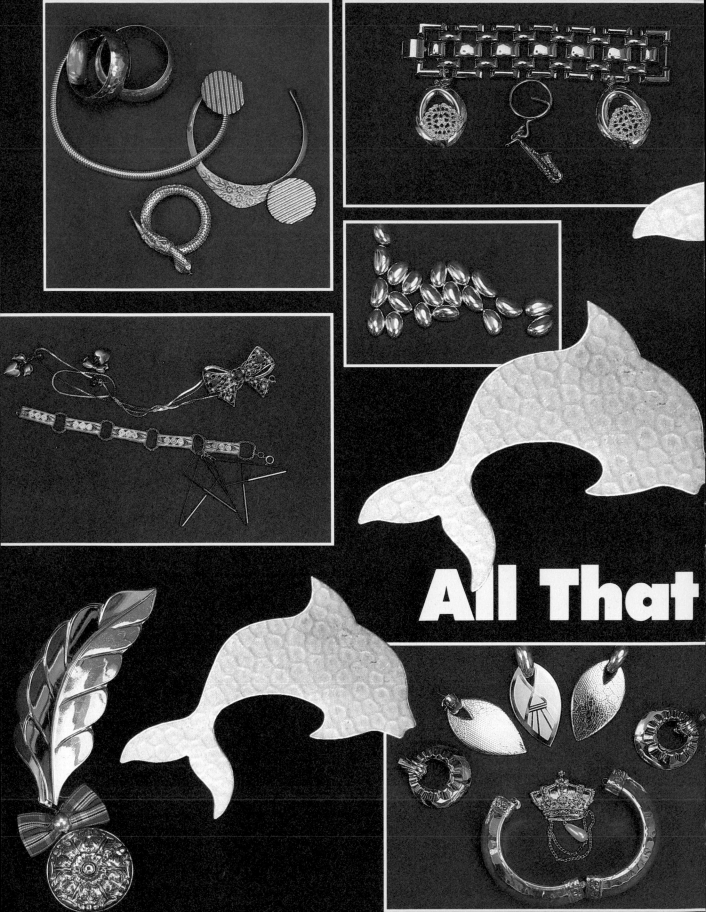

All That

Glitters...

Stockists: Earrings, bracelets etc. from Joe Cool and Flash Trash. Fairy brooch from antique shop. Silver almonds from good confectioners.

Animal Magic!

Did you know that the type of animal you like best can show the secrets of your innermost self?

Decide which of the animals below you'd like best as a pet and discover the real you . . . !

CAT

Cat-lovers are very easy-going people who love to surround themselves with luxury. Your idea of a great night in would be a long, luxurious bath and then a few hours curled up with a good book or TV programme and a box of chocolates.

Often a bit of a loner, you prefer to have just a few very close friends, rather than a large circle of acquaintances and you love nothing more than going out somewhere quiet to talk.

HORSE/PONY

If horses and ponies are your choice, you're a friendly, lively person and though some people might think you a bit 'flighty', you're a very loyal friend to have.

You're not afraid of hard work and once you decide on your chosen career, you'll try everything possible to make it a success. Making up your mind about things is something you find very difficult, though, so you'll probably try a few jobs before you find your ideal.

Easily bored, your friends sometimes have trouble keeping your attention for very long and as you're not very tolerant of others' views you tend to argue quite a lot.

Despite that, though, when the chips are down, you'll do almost anything to help a friend in trouble and would expect them to do the same for you.

When it comes to romance, you tend to be a bit too demanding for most boys and most of your romances end on bad terms.

Try to accept people's bad points (you have some too, you know!), and understand that everyone's life isn't as well-organised as yours.

PARAKEET

Well, you're a bit of a poser, aren't you? Always the first in the street to pick up on a new craze, you love to appear just a little bit 'wacky' to everyone else.

You probably dress quite outrageously and spend a lot of time and money on your clothes, hair and make-up.

You're very outgoing and have lots of friends — your idea of a nightmare is spending a Saturday night in the house with nothing to do and nowhere to go.

You become very bored if you spend a lot of time with the same people so your romances tend to be short, to say the least!

Sitting around doing nothing is impossible for you, so you should try to find a job which involves a lot of travel or working outdoors.

Money is one of your very favourite things, but you're not quite as keen on earning it as you are on spending it — so be careful!

DOG

Energetic and sporty, you're always on the go! You love the outdoor life and spend as much time as possible out of doors.

Friends are attracted by your vivacious personality and you like to have them around as long as things are going your way. But, at the first sign of hassle, you're quite prepared to drop them in favour of someone who's more of a doormat.

It's not easy to annoy you but once you are annoyed, you've got a pretty violent temper and should really try to take things more calmly.

You're very honest — maybe too honest! Sometimes it's better to tell a little white lie than to hurt someone's feelings.

You treat your boyfriends more as friends, so most of your relationships are pretty easy-going and never too serious. That suits you fine, as heavy relationships aren't really your type of thing — anything for a hassle-free life!

RABBIT

If the rabbit is your favourite, you're probably a fairly quiet person with just a few close friends. You sometimes find it quite difficult to make new friends but once you find a good one you'll stick by her through thick and thin.

You're very adaptable and enjoy quiet nights in by the TV just as much as a wild party. Mature and responsible, you have a good relationship with your parents and would much rather discuss things quietly than scream and shout at the top of your voice.

Boys like your romantic nature and you're the type of girl they like to give flowers and chocolates to. Most of your romances are happy ones but be careful you don't allow yourself to be bossed around just to avoid an argument.

You don't like a lot of noise or hustle and bustle around you all the time, so you'd probably be happiest either working on your own or in a small company, maybe working with figures or in administration.

F

READ ALL ABOUT IT!

Patches gives you the once-in-a-lifetime chance to say everything you ever wanted to about your best friend — to their face!

Kate and **Amelia** are old friends, they've known each other for 13 years — but they still have their differences . . .

Amelia's good points — "She thinks the same way that I do. We enjoy the same things and have similar interests."

Bad points — "Amelia's a bit too quiet at times. Like when it comes to making conversation with people, she sort of slips into silence."

Kate's good points — "We have nothing to hide from each other. We're totally relaxed and normal with each other."

Bad points — "Kate's a bit domineering sometimes. When she's talking I often can't get a word in edge ways." (Ohh, ohh . . . we left them arguing over this one!)

Liz and **Cathy** have known each other for five months, but already they've found out each others good and bad points.

Cathy's good points — "Cathy does things on the spur of the moment, she doesn't care and she's a bit mad but I think that's great."

What about her bad points? — "She's VERY impatient and burps really loudly." (Disgusting!)

Liz's good points — "Liz is a good laugh. She's always saying funny things and we have the same sense of humour."

Bad points — "When she gets annoyed she doesn't say a thing, she just sits there and eventually goes to sleep."

Colin and **Steve** have known each other for five years.

Steve's good points — "He's a good laugh and we share the same interests."

Bad points — "Steve's a bit of a show off. Especially when he gets new clothes — it's dead annoying, he wears them to school right away."

Colin's good points — "We've got the same taste in music so we can go to concerts together. He's good fun at parties — always larking about."

Bad points — "He talks too much. And when I get new stuff Colin always puts it down and says it's rubbish." (Huh! And they say girls are bitchy!)

Roberta and **Philip** have known each other five months.

Roberta's good points — "She's very brave really, considering she's quite nervous — she gets on her bike and rides halfway across London."

Bad points — "She's very condescending. Roberta tries to judge people on whether they've had an education or not — as if she thinks a slick voice makes you a better person."

Philip's good points — "I like Philip's innocence and generosity. He's very trusting — naive in the French sense." (What . . . ?)

Bad points — "He does too many favours for people who don't deserve it."

Sarah and **Philip** have known each other for four years — but purely as friends!

Sarah's good points — "She's a good friend to talk to if you've got any problems. Sarah's different, she doesn't follow the crowd and she wears what *she* wants to."

Bad points — "She snaps at me occasionally and her boyfriend can't understand that we're 'just good friends'. She's a bit of a hippy sometimes."

Philip's good points — "He's easy to talk to and has good interests. He always speaks his mind and he's great fun."

Bad points — "Philip's always singing out of tune and comes out with these really stupid comments, like he's always calling me a freak." (Charming!)

Barbara and **J. Nelson** have known each other for just four months. (She wanted to remain anonymous!)

J. Nelson's good points — "I like her dynamic personality. She's fun to go out with and has good taste in clothes and music."

Bad points — "I don't like her smoking, and she's cruel sometimes — she makes me take her phone calls and say she's not in."

Barbara's good points — "She giggles a lot. We've got lots of things in common, like a passion for hot chocolate." (Sounds like my kind of friendship!)

Bad points — "She's a bit evil, but not really horrible, just a little bit when it's absolutely necessary!"

NOBODY'

But if they were, they'd be just like this . . .

THE PERFECT BOYFRIEND . . .

. . . always phones you when he promised he would, and doesn't conjure up rotten excuses like, "I forgot your number . . . honest!" or, "Well there was this big guy with a beard and a bald head wearing a lumberjack shirt and a pair of waterproof trousers who pulled me out of the phone-box and stole my 10p just as I was about to call you."

. . . never gets to the box-office at the local disco and then remembers he's forgotten to bring his money with him, so borrows a fiver from you to pay you in and promises to give you it back as soon as he manages to sell his bike which has been in the newspaper for weeks and no-one's even slightly interested in.

. . . always compliments you about what you're wearing and how pretty you're looking and never tells you that you're putting on weight (even when you are . . .)!

. . . never flirts with any other girls who fancy him and tell him he looks a lot like Ben, Morten, Simon Le Bon etc. (even though he doesn't . . .).

. . . always gives you gifts at Christmas and on your birthday and never buys *you* anything that gives you the sneaking suspicion that he bought it for *himself* knowing that you wouldn't use it or have any desire to want it (e.g. expensive football boots, a season ticket for Man. Utd.).

. . . never leaves you standing outside the pictures for ages while you're getting looks from all your pals from school who think you've been stood-up and then arrives an hour late and says, "Sorry, but there was this big guy with a beard and a bald head who . . ."

. . . always chats away for hours to your mum and dad about how he wants to get a nice safe job in a bank when he leaves school and then offers to do the dishes left over from Sunday lunch.

. . . never moans at you or goes in the huff when you decide to go out with your pals for a dance and never breaks a date with you to go out with *his* mates.

. . . always writes you little romantic notes and gives you flowers.

. . . never comes round to your house and plays his Iron Maiden and Big Country records and always sings along when you put Bananarama or Madonna on.

. . . is completely and utterly boring.

THE PERFECT FRIEND . . .

. . . drops all her other friends and her boyfriend when you're on holiday so she can spend every waking moment following *your* boyfriend around to make sure he doesn't get up to anything with Sindy the Slag.

. . . has exactly the same taste in clothes as you and doesn't mind you having the pick of her wardrobe, but when both of you want the same outfit in Top Shop, she'll lend you the money so *you* can buy it.

. . . looks like Madonna when you want Gorgeous Gary and his mate to notice you but miraculously transforms into a spotty hippo in a sack when Gorgeous Gary comes over to chat one of you up.

S PERFECT

THE PERFECT TEACHER . . .

. . . is younger than you.

. . . doesn't say things like, "You won't get anywhere in this world my girl if you don't smarten yourself up."

. . . believes in things like Self Expression, Doing Your Own Thing, Pupil Power and thinks Exams Are A Fascist Plot.

. . . believes you when you explain that you missed Double Maths because a flying saucer landed just outside the playground and the little green men that came out begged you to go to the planet Vlarg with them and be their ruler, and by the time you'd explained you really had to go to your class now, there you were, forty minutes late, so it wasn't really worthwhile catching the last half hour.

. . . really does think you've written your essay on what you did over the holidays but Steven Spielberg phoned up to borrow it as he wants the storyline for his next film.

. . . rules the class with a limp wave rather than an iron fist.

. . . stands despairingly by while his/ her class sets fire to the curtains/ organises a poker school/superglues the history text books together.

. . . is completely incapable of stopping you reading Patches openly without having to hide it behind a copy of "Arithmetic is Ace".

. . . lets you go home early if you say you think you're about to erupt in contagious purple blotches.

. . . wears baggy brown cords, a sweater with holes in the sleeves, perches on the edge of your desk and says, "Call me Phil."

. . . isn't called Killer Clarke/Ma Duffy/Bald Eagle or Tarty Barty.

. . . tells you that now you're in Sixth Form it's up to you whether you come into school or not.

. . . tells you it doesn't matter whether you pass your exams or not, it's

MORE ON 92 ▶

. . . manages to give you constructive, reasoned, helpful comments when you go shopping and avoids hurting your feelings while still managing to convey that If you buy that fuchsia mini sweater dress, you'll be shunned by anyone· who has the slightest grasp of colour co-ordination and public decency.

. . . refuses to dance with anyone at the disco until she's made sure you've got off with someone first.

. . .will sit and listen for hours while you go into every detail of every sentence your ex-boyfriend ever uttered in your wonderful, never-to-be-forgotten two months together, and she'll never once yawn or absently pick her toe-nails or say things like, "Look, the guy was a slimeball and well you know it."

. . . assures you that Johnny the Biker, who you've been lusting after for months, actually does fancy you even though he's just got engaged to Busty Brenda.

. . . knows everything in the Universe about knitting and sewing and likes nothing better than to run you up an entire new outfit from some old bits of scraggy material you've found lying on the floor of the Needlework Room.

. . . doesn't say things like, "You stupid cow! If I'd known you were going to pour a bottle of red nail varnish all over my leggings, I'd never have let you borrow them. Well, you'll just have to buy me a new pair and I'll never lend you anything again! Ever!"

. . . tells the blond guy at the disco with the Bruce Willis grin and the nice bum that she doesn't go out with boys but that her friend's been eyeing him up for yonks and she's just sitting over there and why doesn't he go and buy her a Coke?

. . . isn't one of those people who can eat three Indian takeways a night and still look like a stick insect.

. . . lets you copy her Maths homework, then, when you're caught out, tells the Maths teacher (whose nickname is Godzilla) that it was she who persuaded you to let her copy your perfecty done Maths homework because Maths is your favourite of all subjects and you're so good at it.

. . . isn't called Ethel or Hilda or Betty.

. . . only fancies boys you don't fancy.

. . . doesn't exist!

It's not like smoking or drinking. You can refuse to buy cigarettes. You can physically remove them from your presence. But you are permanently attached to your nails.

The last resolution I made about my nails was on December the first, and really it was all down to Dave Thomson, although he didn't know it, of course. Dave is a friend of my friend Gemma's brother Colin, if you follow me. I met him at Gemma's house, and fell for him instantly. He has dark curly hair and dark brown eyes and the nicest smile you have ever seen in your life. And he was going to be around for Christmas.

I was tempted to go out and buy false nails there and then, but I stopped myself. False nails are exactly what they say they are. False. I would not start off what I hoped would develop into an interesting relationship on a false note. I would stop biting my nails.

It was excruciatingly difficult. Not only can you not detach yourself from your fingers, but you often find yourself nibbling quite unconsciously, and by the time you realise what's happening it's too late.

Gemma is a good friend but not always completely understanding.

"I just don't see the attraction. I can't imagine why anyone would want to do it."

"You don't *want* to. It's a nervous thing. Anyway, who are you to talk? You're still smoking fifteen a day."

"I'm going to stop at New Year. Let me enjoy Christmas first."

By the middle of December my nails were quite reasonable. They were neat and even, and nearly all of them had a white rim at the top. Extremely narrow, of course, but *there*. I was helped by the fact that the exams were over — always a stress point — and I had nothing to worry about except how I was going to afford everyone's Christmas present. And I had such a lot to look forward to. Especially the party.

Gemma and her brother were having a party two days before Christmas. And along with about fifty people, Dave Thomson was going to be there. I took a lot of trouble over my appearance. I always do for a party, but this time I was even more particular. I bought a new

A READER'S TRUE STORY

I FIND myself making resolutions regularly, throughout the year, not just on New Year's Day. Quite often it's the same resolution. Usually it's to do with my nails. It's a dreadful thing to be old enough for college and still be addicted to biting your nails.

My mother has been nagging me for my entire life about my nails.

"It looks *dreadful*," she'd say, "and it's so irritating to *watch*."

"Don't look, then," I'd reply, and she'd go on about my impudence.

But people don't realise how hard it is.

NEW

I was sure Dave wouldn't fancy me with a fistful of chewed nails. So I decided I was going to stop . . .

BEGINNINGS

dress; black velvet with a deep V at the back. I don't have a weight problem, and the dress looked great, although I say it myself. My sister, Alison, does have a weight problem. She was jealous as sin when I walked in and swanned up and down in front of my family, my hair blonde and glossy, and my new Red Alert lipstick adding a dash of colour. Dad grumbled a bit about the backless style, but I could tell he was impressed. Mum was the one who surprised me.

"Here," she said, holding out a small paper bag. "It was supposed to go in your stocking but maybe you should have it now."

It was a tiny bottle, Red Alert nail varnish.

"You've done really well with your nails, Sarah. Why don't you flash them about a bit?"

I would have kissed her, except that it would have ruined my lipstick. Mothers are surprising sometimes.

•

The party was brilliant. There were all sorts of games which I didn't think I'd like and which turned out to be hilarious. The food was great, and the company fantastic. I played it very cool with Dave Thomson. Someone who looked the way I looked, with the new black dress and the fabulous nails, could afford to play hard to get; at least for ten minutes or so.

I seemed to get it just right, for by half past ten he was chatting me up.

We chatted a bit about various things — fairly ordinary subjects like college. We had just finished discussing the Christmas edition of Top of the Pops, when he said, "Would you come out with me some time? I could get my dad's car and we could go to a disco or something. How about it?"

I pretended to consider. Then I said, "Sure. Why not?", and hoped he didn't notice the trouble I was having keeping the excitement out of my voice.

"I have to stick around with the family for the next few days — I suppose you'll be doing that yourself — but I'll phone after Christmas. How about Wednesday? Will you be in if I phone on Wednesday?"

"Well, things get a bit hectic this time of year, but I should be home, some of the time at least."

"OK. I'll phone you."

The conversation carried on but I

didn't take in any more.

Christmas was really nice, as usual. My granny came to stay, as she always does. For all she's so ancient she's a really sharp dresser, and very up to date about things. We get along great.

She could tell I was uptight about Wednesday's phone call without me saying anything, but she didn't make any of those crass remarks about boyfriends that parents are particularly prone to. And since she had guessed so much in the first place, she was not slow to imagine the cause of my anxiety as the day and the evening of that Wednesday slowly wore on without the promised phone call. By eleven o'clock I was really upset. Not only had Dave failed to ring, but in my nervousness I had massacred two finger nails, quite unconsciously.

"That's a pity," said my granny. "They were looking terrific. But you know, the great thing about nails is that you always get another chance. They always grow again."

I looked at her hands, with their slightly pudgy fingers and neat pointed nails, painted a pearly pink, a real grandmother colour. What could she possibly know about it?

"I used to bite my nails too. Did you know that?"

I have never ever heard an adult admit to that. They don't admit to much anyway, but I've never heard any older person admit to something like that. My astonishment must have shown.

"Oh, yes," she said. "I was much, much older than you when I gave it up."

"What stopped you?"

"False teeth."

I couldn't help laughing. She was funny, but apart from making me feel temporarily more cheerful, she was no help at all. False teeth were just too drastic a remedy, even in my desperate state.

Dave didn't phone the whole of Thursday, and by then I was ready to gnash my entire left hand. I did lose the pinkie, but that was all, which showed colossal restraint, let me tell you.

He phoned on Friday night, just as I had agreed to go out with Gemma because the tension was getting me down. He sounded breathless, as if he'd been running.

I was dead cool. Although I say it myself, I was impressive. My granny

passed me in the hallway with all her fingers crossed in case my somewhat distant manner backfired on me and he hung up. But he didn't. The poor soul had been stuck with relatives for two whole days longer than he had bargained for, hundreds of miles away.

"You could have phoned," I reminded him, softening just fractionally.

"I'd left your number at home, your address, everything. I wasn't even sure of your last name."

I wasn't surprised at that. My last name is Polish in origin and an absolute burden on occasions like these.

"I'm really sorry. Will you still come out with me?"

"When?"

"Tonight?"

"Ah. Well, Gemma and I are going to the cinema tonight."

"Tomorrow?"

I pretended to think. My granny passed again and crossed her eyes this time.

"Yes. OK, that would be fine."

My granny uncrossed everything, and went all limp, like a witch suddenly drained of her power to work magical spells. She sagged against the wall and staggered off into the kitchen. I giggled down the phone.

"What's the joke?" asked Dave.

"It's just my granny. She's a head banger."

"I see," he said, but he clearly didn't.

"I'll explain tomorrow. When shall I meet you?"

•

Dave and I have been going together ever since then. New Year was truly brilliant. Life is wonderful at the moment. Dave is wonderful, college is wonderful, the weather is wonderful, even if it's freezing rain. The most wonderful thing about Dave, among several wonderful things, is that he either hasn't noticed my nail problem, or else it doesn't bother him. And the problem is getting much better. I'm really sticking to my December the first resolution. And I'm a whole month ahead of everyone else. My sister Alison has gone on a low calorie diet and is permanently ravenous. Gemma has given up cigarettes and is permanently bad tempered. But I think they'll make it. Let's face it, if I can do it, anyone can!

FEEDBACK
S P E C I A L

You know the rules — discover the answer to each question, take all the first letters and unscramble them to solve the problem . . .

No money prizes this time because it's the annual, but it's worth getting the practice in!

The answers are there just in case you're a cheat!

A) The title of a No. 1 hit for a popular synth duo . . .
1) The pale-faced chiefess of The Banshees.
2) Julian Cope made a bouncing return to the charts with this mini-classic . . .
3) It was boots on and rifles polished as Status Quo stood to attention . . .
4) The title of Swing Out Sister's No. 1 debut album . . .
5) The Beastie Boys couldn't get any rest with this hit . . .
6) The cheeky foursome who cycled their way around Prince's 'Kiss' . . .
7) Duran Duran were prepared to wait 'til the morning after with this chart ballad . . .

B) Discover the name of this chart-topping female artist . . .
1) U.2 gave themselves away with this first single lifted from 'The Joshua Tree' . . .
2) This man is a 'Real Wild Child' . . .
3) The debut album from Sheffield's A.B.C. . . .
4) Curiosity Killed The Cat didn't want you to come any closer with the title of their first L.P. . . .

5) Ol' Terence Trent D'Arby didn't want kicked out in the streets with this Top Ten hit . . .
6) This duo from Hackney scored highly with their hits 'Respectable' and 'FLM' . . .
7) Record label home for David Bowie, Queen and The Beatles . . .
8) Ms Harry, whose band was named after her hair colour . . .

C) Find the name of a top-selling solo male singer . . .
1) This girl wooed them on to the dancefloors with hits like 'Toy Boy' and 'So Macho' . . .
2) A-ha's first hit in the U.K . . .
3) Ol' 'King Thumb' Mark King fronts this four-piece chart band of funksters.
4) Sting promised he'd be watching you with his Number One hit . . .
5) Ben and his crew charmed our hearts with 'Misfit' and 'Down To Earth' . . .
6) U.2's record label . . .
7) Have they split up or not? Mick Jagger and Keith Richards aren't prepared to say . . .
8) Vince Clarke and Alison Moyet made

up this successful pop duo of the eighties . . .
9) The little woman with the high voice who first burst on to the scene with 'Wuthering Heights' . . .
10) The men responsible for 'When Smokey Sings' and 'The Night You Murdered Love' . . .

D) The name of an all-singing, all-dancing family group . . .
1) Prince didn't want to go alone with this hit from his 'Purple Rain' album . . .
2) Corinne Drewery fronts this swinging trio . . .
3) They had a vicious snapping hit in 1986 with 'Calling All The Heroes' . . .
4) Record label home for Simple Minds, P.I.L. and Genesis . . .
5) Annie Lennox and Dave Stewart — otherwise known as . . .
6) Bryan, the man who fronted Roxy Music . . .
7) She duetted with George Michael on 'I Knew You Were Waiting' . . .
8) They teamed up with Aerosmith and told you to 'Walk This Way' . . .

E) Well-known D.J. . . .
1) Wayne Hussey and Co. who produced 'Wasteland' and 'Stay With Me' . . .
2) You couldn't tear Taffy away from her transistor . . .
3) This band's debut album was 'First (The Sound Of Music)' . . .
4) This guy claimed it was 'Hip To Be Square' . . .
5) The band that opened up the 'Picture Book' . . .
6) Mags, Pal and . . .
7) This age-old Tom Jones hit burst into the charts again in 1987 . . .
8) The Madonna-produced debut from the king of Levi's 501's . . .
9) Along with his Coconuts, this man scored hits with 'Annie, I'm Not Your Daddy' and 'Stool Pigeon' . . .

ANSWERS

A) 'IT'S A SIN'
1) Siouxsie 2) Trampoline' 3) 'In The Army Now' 4) 'It's Better To Travel' 5) 'No Sleep Til Brooklyn' 6) Age Of Chance 7) 'Save A Prayer'

B) KIM WILDE
1) 'With Or Without You' 2) Iggy Pop 3) 'Lexicon Of Love' 4) 'Keep Your Distance' 5) 'If You Let Me Stay' 6) Mel And Kim 7) E.M.I. 8) Debbie

C) RICK ASTLEY
1) Sinitta 2) 'Take On Me' 3) Level 42 4) 'Every Breath You Take' 5) Curiosity Killed The Cat 6) Island 7) Rolling Stones 8) Yazoo 9) Kate Bush 10) A.B.C.

D) FIVE STAR
1) 'Take Me With U' 2) Swing Out Sister 3) It Bites 4) Virgin 5) Eurythmics 6) Ferry 7) Aretha Franklin 8) Run D.M.C.

E) MIKE SMITH
1) Mission 2) 'I Love My Radio' 3) Then Jericho 4) Huey Lewis 5) Simply Red 6) Morten 7) 'It's Not Unusual' 8) 'Each Time You Break My Heart' 9) Kid Creole.

1. A crumpled blouse and gaudy skirt might not seem much of a bargain even if you did get them for fifty pence and the lady on the stall told you the blouse was pure silk. But, if you lop a few inches off the hem of the skirt and team it up with black, you're not going to be mistaken for a pair of old curtains.

2. Size 16 suits are a regular feature at jumble sales and even your mum wouldn't claim that you'll grow into it. Chop the dress in half and take some seams up the back until you've got a rather sophisticated pencil skirt. The boxy jacket shouldn't need much doing to it, except for taking the sleeves up. After washing and ironing, the blouse does indeed turn out to be silk, and a rather posh accompaniment for this plain suit.

Ever wondered why it is that when you and your mate go to a jumble sale, she emerges with a complete new wardrobe and you come out trailing a bin-bag full of old rags? Well, you'll have to invest a little imagination to turn your finds into something wearable.

2nd
A

4. Going to a party? Yes, you'll look a perfect sack of potatoes in this baggy dress. Out with the needle and thread again . . . Follow the original seams on the dress, taking it in to fit you. Team it up with long gloves and high heels and you're ready to face anything.

So, the next time you spend a morning picking up bargains, wash and iron them, then spend a little time considering how you can convert them into clothes, before you offer them to your mum as dusters!

3. Dated suede coats are another regular find on the stalls. Fifties print tops and baggy long-johns along with scabby old vanity cases cram the benches too. Buy a couple of suede coats and use the material from one to cover your vanity case. Use leather glue (you can get it from ironmongers) to stick the suede down, and then take the scissors to the second coat to turn it into a jacket. You'll have to stitch the lining up, but you'll be able to hem the suede with leather glue as well. Pull up a belt on your long-johns and they'll miraculously turn into leggings.

TIME ROUND

◄ FROM 85

much more important to be a nice person.

. . . does everything you tell him because you once saw him at a staff night out with his trousers on his head, doing an impression of the Headmaster.

. . . makes sure you do so badly at your exams you get classed as a complete drongo, get put into Atilla the Hun's class with all the other dum-dums and are given hours of lessons and homework until you learn how to write your own name.

THE PERFECT GIRLFRIEND . . .

. . . will believe her boyfriend when he tells her that the long blonde hairs on his jacket belong to his next-door-neighbour's Afghan Hound.

. . . has a great sense of humour and thinks there's nothing funnier than having ice-cubes or fat black hairy spiders dropped down the back of her dress.

. . . thinks a great day out consists of watching Tottenham Hotspur play in the pouring rain, followed by a visit to Mad Max VIII at the local fleapit and a bag of soggy chips eaten in a bus shelter on the way home.

. . . enjoys friendly chats with her boyfriend's ex-girlfriends (who all look like Madonna) but isn't even on speaking terms with her ex-boyfriends and walks past them in the street.

. . . sits at home looking at photographs and playing soppy records which remind her of him, while the man in her life is living it up with his mates in a sweaty disco in San Antonio.

. . . doesn't complain when her boyfriend buys himself a pair of Levi 501's, a gigantic Samantha Fox poster and a fishing rod and then asks her to pay him into the cinema because he's skint.

. . . always looks great but never has to stay in to colour her hair, give herself a manicure or use a face-pack.

. . . loves Indian food (just like her boyfriend does) and manages to consume one beef curry and nan bread a night without putting on any weight.

. . . is fascinated by the innards of cars and motorbikes and enjoys nothing more than spending her weekend in a greasy garage wearing overalls and listening to her boyfriend describe the intricate workings of a 1000cc Yamahoto.

. . . understands totally that a night out at the swankiest restaurant in town just can't compete with watching the World Boxing Championship on T.V.

. . . has "I am a mug, please walk on me" tattooed on her forehead.

THE PERFECT PARENTS . . .

. . . don't say things like, "What time of night do you call this? I told you to tidy up that room before you went out. You needn't think you're going anywhere looking like that! You're not setting foot outside this house, my girl, until you've done your homework."

. . . haven't got degrees in subjects like Mild Head-Nipping, including sections on Bedrooms, Clothes and Music; Serious Nagging; Dealing with Money; Timekeeping and Boyfriends; and Really Heavy Threats and How To Carry Them Out Effectively.

. . . don't "understand what it's like to be young". If they *did*, you'd be in big trouble!

. . . are on hand with mugs of tea, Kleenex and choccie biccies and don't once say, "I warned you about that boy" when you come home soggy and red-eyed after being packed in by the two-timing rat.

. . . always slip you a fiver for a taxi home from the disco even though they know your mate's dad is picking you up.

. . . are gullible fools. As in . . .

"Come on, Julie, you'll be late for school!"

"Aw, Mum, I can't be bothered today. It's only Maths and Chemistry and I'm going to fail them anyway."

"OK then. Why don't you have

another hour in bed, and then we can go shopping. You need some new gear for the disco tomorrow night, don't you . . .?"

Or . . .

"Mum! It's Julie. I've missed the last bus, so I'm going to be a bit late."

"That's OK, love, I'll leave the key under the mat for you."

Or . . .

explaining to your father, when he catches you wrapped round your latest boyfriend on the doorstep, that he's just a mate . . . "Actually, he really likes Tracey, Dad — we've just worked out a little scheme to make her jealous . . ." *And he believes it!!*

. . . approve of your latest Madonna outfit.

. . . think Jon Bon Jovi is the greatest talent since Cliff Richard.

. . . give you regular pocket money rises without you having to whine or grovel or show willing by doing paper rounds and visiting old ladies.

. . . do your homework for you.

. . . write you sick notes.

. . . like *all* your friends except Debbie who wears Crimplene twin sets and wants to be a missionary.

. . . don't make you sneak out of the house in the longest coat known to man so that your extramegamini skirt will pass unnoticed.

. . . know you like to look your best and provide you with your own make-up artist so you no longer have to take your make-up out with you and trowel it on in the loos.

. . . don't believe in homework and write sharp letters to teachers saying that they certainly won't let *their* daughter waste her evenings writing about Life In A Drop Of Pond Water and memorising useless nonsense like Atomic Tables.

. . . take all the fun out of saying things like, "I wouldn't be seen *dead* in that, Mum! You really haven't a clue, have you?" Or, "What do you mean you don't understand it? Everybody knows the square of the hypotenuse is equal to the sum of the squares on the other two sides! What are you, thick or something?"

THE PERFECT SISTER . . .

. . . tells you to help yourself to her make-up, hairspray, tights and clothes any time you want and you don't even have to ask.

. . . doesn't think she's doing you a favour if she gives you her cast-off puffball skirt she looks like a ballet-dancing elephant in anyway.

. . . encourages you to dress like Madonna and flirt with her tasty boyfriend because she understands that you're doing him a favour by making him realise there are a lot of better-looking girls around than your sister.

. . . lives in Ulan Bator.

. . . says things to your dad like, "But *I* never came to any harm when I went to the all-night disco at the Biker's club. It's just like a tea party, really."

. . . is aged eighteen months and gurgles cutely in her pram as you wheel her round the football pitch in the hope that *he'll* notice you.

. . . tells your mother that she doesn't want to go to the disco with you because she's far too young for that sort of nonsense and can she have a new dolly blanket to sew?

. . . will allow you to try out fake tan/home perms/highlighting kits on her first, so that if they're a disaster, it's *her* hair that falls out and *her* skin that turns bright orange.

. . . is such a total dimbo at

everything from Maths to keeping her room tidy, there's not a cat's chance that anyone will ever say, "I wish you could be more like your sister."

. . . doesn't say things like, "I'm going to tell Mum you sneaked in at three o'clock last night and you're wearing that stupid scarf because you've got three lovebites on your neck."

. . . is three years older than you and has kept every test paper and exam paper she was ever set at your school so some of them are bound to come up again.

. . . has an Honours degree in English, can copy your handwriting exactly and likes nothing better than to help you out by writing 1000 words on, "Why Shakespeare Was A Tory" for your sociology class.

. . . has a wardrobe full of clothes which fit you perfectly, but has the sort of figure which makes your clothes look like tight dishrags on her.

. . . tells your parents you spent all evening doing macramé with her at the Community Centre so you couldn't possibly have been seen hanging about the street corner shouting, "Get them off, Nigel!"

. . . is married to Michael J. Fox's brother.

. . . understands that you need *some* company when you're baby-sitting for her so insists you always invite your mates round for a party.

. . . is someone else's.

Then I had a brainwave . . .

Soon . . .

Then . . .